It gives me a very real sense of personal delight to introduce you to the Official Event Guide for The Tall Ships Races 2010 – Hartlepool.

I am proud to say that my involvement with this international event dates back to 2005 when we, as a town, welcomed 37 Tall Ships en route to the Newcastle/Gateshead Quayside. We did what we do best back then, and that's working in strong partnership with others, to achieve an amazing event for all the crew involved and for the 175,000 visitors that came along to soak up the atmosphere.

That success led to an invitation by the race organisers Sail Training International to bid to host a leg of this annual spectacle. Within a few short weeks we delivered a bid that was incredibly well received and on the 28th June 2006, we learned that the town of Hartlepool had been chosen as the destination port for The Tall Ships Races 2010.

Together with PD Teesport and Hartlepool Marina Ltd we have worked tirelessly since then to prepare our town for the fleet of ships, their tired and hungry crew and for you our valued visitors. We aim to make this event memorable for all involved with it.

There is a strong connection with The Tall Ships Races in North East England and Hartlepool's relationship with the sea is inextricable. The docks and quays which welcome the mighty fleet today were created over 150 years ago by local industrialists and entrepreneurs including Sir William Gray and Ralph Ward Jackson. The legacy of their enterprise forms the setting for the coming celebrations, enhanced by recent developments all around the marina including Hartlepool's Maritime Experience and the quality dining experiences at Navigation Point which add up to a world-class environment to enjoy.

I thank you for your support for The Tall Ships Races 2010 – Hartlepool and I do hope you return to our proud town again and again for many years to come.

Stuart Drummond
Mayor of Hartlepool

be part of it!

PARTNERS AND FUNDERS

SPONSORS

Diamond

Platinum

Gold

Silver

Silver

Bronze

Bronze

FRIENDS

A Secret Garden

Hartlepool & District Flower Club

Rachel Gretton Glass

Van Dalen Recycling

Wynyard | Park

PARTNERS

Official Commercial Media Sponsor

Official Sponsor of Fireworks

Hartlepool Mail
Official Local Media Partner

Sponsor of the Official Souvenir DVD

LIVING NORTH
Official Event Guide Partner

mobeus
Official Trophy Designer

NHS Hartlepool
Official Sponsor of Change 4 Life Marquee

OFFICIAL MERCHANDISING LTD
make sure it's official
Official Merchandising Partner

Radio Hartlepool 102.4fm
Official Local Media Partner

Robert Usher Photography
Offical Photographer

NOMINATED CHARITIES

Hartlepool & District Hospice • Hartlepool Sea Cadets
Royal National Lifeboat Institute

SPECIAL THANKS TO

All Infrastructure Contractors • Belfast Host Port
Black Diamond of Durham • British Red Cross
Cameron's Brewery • Cleveland Fire Brigade
Cleveland Police • Coastguard • Grand Central
Hartlepool Borough Council Staff • Hartlepool Business Forum
Hartlepool Divers' Club • Hartlepool Primary Care Trust
Hartlepool Schools and Colleges • Hartlepool Sea Cadets
Hartlepool UFC • Hatton Traffic Management
Highways Agency • Liverpool Host Port • Mandale
MLA Renaissance North East • Network Rail
NewcastleGateshead Host Port • North East Ambulance Service
Northern Rail • North Tees and Hartlepool Acute Foundation Trust
Old West Quay • Richmond Event Management • RNLI • Schroder
Seymour (Civil Engineering Contractors) ltd • Spirul
St John Ambulance • Topsail Events and Charter
Touchline Event Management • visitTeesvalley
Val Johnson, Stonelemon Ltd • Vue Cinema • West View Project

Federation of Small Businesses
The UK's Leading Business Organisation

NAVIGATE A PROSPEROUS FUTURE WITH THE FSB

The FSB is proud to be one of the leading supporters and Diamond Sponsor of the Tall Ships 2010 event. As the UK's largest business organisation, over 213,000 small businesses nationwide have already set sail on their business journey with the FSB.

COME ALONG AND SEE WHAT TREASURES YOU CAN UNEARTH!

Come and visit the FSB Marquee which is located in the Earth Zone in the Tall Ships Village.

The FSB Marquee is a vibrant and interactive trading area for a wide and varied range of local businesses, showcasing their goods and services to the thousands of Tall Ships visitors...
There really is something for everyone so please do come and see what is on offer!

WANT TO FIND OUT MORE ABOUT JOINING THE FSB?

Visit our Information Stand in the FSB Marquee and find out how you can 'get on board' and 'set sail' on your own business journey with the FSB.

Discover how the FSB can help you and your business navigate a safe path to a prosperous future. With a wealth of member benefits such as FREE legal help 24 hours a day 365 days a year; FREE business banking and an FSB Care facility; the FSB is there to assist you and save you money.

We give our members the chance to have their voice heard! The FSB's Policy Units throughout the UK work hard to secure better conditions and concessions for the small business community by applying pressure on politicians, government and civil servants in Parliament, regional agencies and local authorities.

For further information on joining the FSB, visit the FSB Marquee in the Earth Zone or contact NE Regional Organiser, David Longstaff on david.longstaff@fsb.org.uk or 01609 773038 or visit the website at www.fsb.org.uk.

A selection of FSB Business Benefits and Service Providers

 **LEGAL PROTECTION SCHEME**

Insurance for legal and professional fees, plus legal and taxation advice
In association with

 BUSINESS BANKING

Exclusive free business banking designed for small businesses offering a number of unique features
In association with

The **co-operative** bank
good with money

 MERCHANT SERVICE

Exclusive card acceptance service available to FSB members at competitive, discounted rates
In association with

✖ RBS WorldPay

 **INSURANCE SERVICE**

Hassle-free insurance and advice
In association with

 ▲towergate

 TELECOM

Significant savings on fixed and mobile call charges
In association with

daisy

 IFS

Offers members access to a wide range of financial services
In association with

 **Share the Secret!**
FSB. The Leading Business Organisation

THERE HAS NEVER BEEN A MORE IMPORTANT TIME TO TELL YOUR BUSINESS COLLEAGUES AND FRIENDS ABOUT THE FSB

Water, water, everywhere...

with plenty a drop to drink!

"When there's the potential for a million people to descend on a town, what goes on underground can be as vital as what happens overground to ensure everyone has a great time."

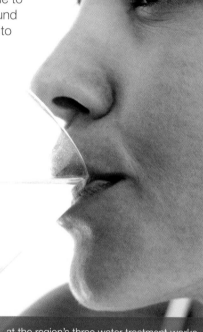

So says Tom Norman of Hartlepool Water, one of the sponsors of this year's Tall Ships Races.

"One of the most important things that goes on under our feet, all day every day, is fresh water coursing through mains and pipes before it arrives at our taps. And with such a large number of people heading to Hartlepool to see the Tall Ships, getting the right amount of water to the right locations is crucial."

On a typical day, Hartlepool Water supplies around 33 million litres of water to 90,000 people in the Borough of Hartlepool. All of Hartlepool's drinking water comes from underground, pumped from 19 boreholes sunk deep into the limestone rock at eleven sites across the region. The water is blended at the region's three water treatment works prior to supply, to ensure it meets appropriate standards for drinking.

"Because our water comes from underground aquifers and is filtered through many layers of limestone before it reaches us, it's of a very high purity," says Tom. "Our treatment works provide the finishing touches, before it's sent to customers."

"We're really proud that our town has attracted the Tall Ships Races," says Tom. "These guys are no strangers to the challenges water can throw at them. Rather than navigating across it, our challenge is getting it from one point to another. It's a very different challenge, but getting it right is just as crucial."

www.hartlepoolwater.co.uk

Contents

Welcome from the Mayor of Hartlepool 1

The Tall Ships Races 2010 9

Getting Around The Site 14

The Tall Ships Races - Event Programme 17-35

Travel and Transport 36

Inspirational Hartlepool 39-55

The Tall Ships Story 41

The Volunteer Movement 57

Welcome to the Tees Valley and Come Back Soon 58

Tees Valley Events 61

Tall Ships A-Z 63-131

North Sea Tall Ships Regatta 133

Memorabilia Stamps 134

Official Merchandise 138

Top Tips 141

Competition and 2 for 1 Offer 142

Site Plan 144

Tees Valley
unlimited

Front Cover image: tallshipstock.com Stad Amsterdam

Photography: Gary Kester, Ken Cowins, Mike Kipling, Dennis Weller, Harland Deer, Chris Armstrong, Hartlepool Borough Council, One NorthEast and tallshipstock.com

All details in this brochure are correct at the time of printing, Hartlepool Borough Council cannot be held responsible for any inaccuracies contained within.

The official guide to The Tall Ships Races 2010 has been designed and produced with Hartlepool Borough Council by Living North Ltd. 5 Cattle Market, Hexham, NE46 1NJ. www.livingnorth.com Tel: 01434 609933

Proud to be part of The Tall Ships Race

For over 80 years award-winning Yuill Homes have been known for innovation and design excellence throughout the North East. We have built our reputation on creating desirable and quality homes that stand the test of time.

We are proud and delighted to be sponsoring the Tall Ships Race and look forward to welcoming the vessels into our home town of Hartlepool.

Yuill Homes welcomes The Tall Ships Race

Currently building quality homes at the following locations:

Hartlepool
Tel: 08456 437209

Billingham
Tel: 08456 437202

Middlesbrough
Tel: 08456 437207

Murton
Tel: 08456 437204

Consett
Tel: 08456 437203

Blaydon, Gateshead
Tel: 08456 437205

Longbenton, Newcastle
Tel: 08456 437201

Coming Soon

Beadnell
Tel: 07860 503069

Great Ayton
Tel: 01429 266620

Thornley
Tel: 07738 195123

Whitby
Tel: 01429 266620

Sales Centres & Showhomes open Thurs-Mon 11am-5pm

yuillhomes.co.uk

Photography for illustrative purposes only.

 YUILL HOMES

THE NORTH SEA COAST'S STRATEGIC ROLE IN THE UK'S MARINE RENEWABLE ENERGY

The North East is a prime location and plays a significant role in developing the UK's offshore wind industry. This growth industry can bring jobs, both on and offshore, and also investment to the region.

Offshore wind is playing a significant role in delivering the government's 2020 renewable energy targets. The Crown Estate has extensive marine assets throughout the UK as it owns virtually the entire seabed out to 12 nautical miles, including the rights to explore and utilise the natural resources of the UK continental shelf (excluding oil, gas and coal). We have utilised the UK's advantageous geographical position to harness offshore wind power. This has included four leasing rounds of the seabed for offshore wind farm development which in total, including existing, and new offshore wind renewable energy programmes, could provide up to 48GW by 2020-5, more than 40 per cent of the UK total electricity requirements. We are working with all stakeholders including government departments, developers and utilities, in realising the UK government's targets for renewable energy. The UK is leading the world with 1GW installed offshore wind capacity.

The largest of the leasing rounds is Round 3, which alone aims to deliver a quarter of the UK's total electricity needs by 2020. Three of the nine Round 3 zones are in the North Sea which means that ports all along the North East coast could play a significant part, not only in the construction but also in the operation and maintenance. Round 3 is one of the largest infrastructure projects in the world and it is estimated that £100 billion will be invested in this industry and between 50,000 -70,000 jobs could be generated by the UK offshore wind industry in this decade. The developers for these zones require a full, new planning application including an Environmental Impact Assessment and a full consultation. The Crown Estate will only grant a lease allowing construction to start when statutory consents have been obtained from appropriate decision-making bodies.

With our role being laid down by Parliament: to enhance the value of the estates we manage and to earn a surplus for the benefit of the UK taxpayer and annually contribute over £200 million to the Treasury, offshore wind can benefit the UK both economically and also provide a secure alternative energy supply.

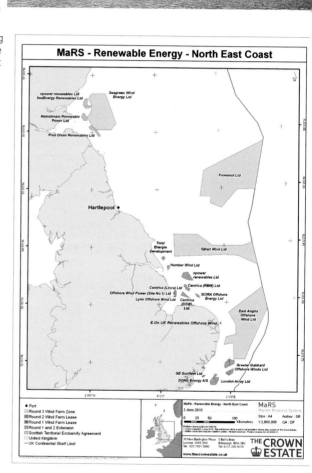

MaRS - Renewable Energy - North East Coast

THE CROWN ESTATE

16 New Burlington Place • London • W1S 2HX • Tel: 020 7851 5080
Email: marineestate@thecrownestate.co.uk • www.thecrownestate.co.uk

All set for ENGLAND'S
biggest free event in 2010

Hartlepool is proud and delighted to have been chosen as the finishing port and only UK host port for The Tall Ships Races 2010. This celebratory event is expected to see up to 1 million visitors coming to Hartlepool.

The Tall Ships Races are an internationally acclaimed, annual competition presented by Szczecin and organised by Sail Training International. They are held every summer in European waters with between 60 and 100 vessels from 15–20 countries taking part. These vessels are crewed by some 2000 – 3000 young people from over 30 countries worldwide. The main aim of the event is to provide an opportunity for young people to develop their personal skills in a challenging environment. Therefore at least 50% of a Tall Ship's crew must be aged between 15 and 25.

The Tall Ships Races 2010 will visit the four diverse ports of Antwerp, Aalborg, Kristiansand and Hartlepool, all of which have a long maritime history. For centuries each of the four ports has been visited by both commercial and leisure sailors, so they are more than suited to handle the competitive demands of The Tall Ships Races. Having experience of hosting maritime events for a number of years, each port has the capacity, marine skills and expertise to provide a fantastic Tall Ships experience for Captains, crew and visitors alike. Each place has its own stories to tell and warm welcome to offer, producing a combined experience that is sure to be unforgettable.

www.tallshipsraces.com

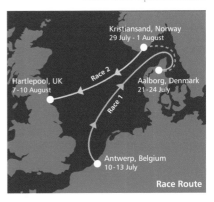

Kristiansand, Norway
29 July - 1 August

Hartlepool, UK
7 - 10 August

Race 2

Aalborg, Denmark
21 - 24 July

Race 1

Antwerp, Belgium
10 - 13 July

Race Route

The Flemish city of Antwerp is the first port of call (10th–13th July). It is the second largest port in Europe and offers an appealing combination of stunning architecture, fashionable boutiques, traditional pubs, stately monuments, sophisticated clubs, inspired artworks and restaurants whose tables are piled with plates of delicious food. Antwerp also boasts a wealth of outstanding museums, picturesque galleries, refreshing greenery and urban haunts.

From there it is on to Aalborg (21st–24th July) whose modern harbour front has already greeted The Tall Ships Races in 1999 and 2004. The new cultural centre Nordkraft and the Utzon Centre will be ready to host many exciting activities for the crews. Aalborg is known as a festive and hospitable city which knows how to celebrate life and greets visitors with open arms, all set against the backdrop of amazing scenery.

Kristiansand is the next stop (29th July–1st August). With its long seafaring tradition it offers a vibrant and industrial commercial life and even boasts its own fully rigged ship, the Sorlandet. South Norway's sheltered coastline is famous for its thousands of small, low lying islands and skerries. Kristiansand is one of Norway's largest and most attractive ports and all the ships will be berthed only a five minute walk from the vibrant city centre.

At last, the Tall Ships will sail into Hartlepool (7th–10th August) where we will be delighted and honoured to be the final host port. Hartlepool is a proud and passionate town with the sea in its blood! The town represents a rich mix of the very old and the very new, with its historic landmarks dating back to the 14th century. But it is predominantly right at the heart of Hartlepool – an area that has benefited from a £500 million regeneration initiative, breathing new life into Hartlepool's maritime heritage, where The Tall Ships Races will take place. Hartlepool Marina is the jewel in Hartlepool's crown offering a wealth of activities for visitors and locals alike – it also houses our very own Tall Ship, HMS Trincomalee. During the event, Hartlepool will become a temporary home for the magnificent fleet of Tall Ships. Between the two berthing sites of Victoria Harbour and the Marina will be The Tall Ships Village. Split into three zones, it will provide a fantastic mix of international street theatre, music, trade stalls, exhibitions and food from around the world.

It is anticipated that hosting the event will create a genuine, catalytic impact upon the regeneration of the town. We can't wait to host The Tall Ships Races and hope the event will be as memorable and successful as possible for everyone!

BBC TEES

For full coverage of the Tall Ships event, as well as the very latest traffic and travel, tune into BBC Tees 95FM & DAB

* Enable Bluetooth© on your mobile device to receive regular updates while in the Tall Ships Village.

BBC LOOK NORTH

Look North will bring you all the colour of the event on BBC One

Weekdays: 6.30pm
Saturday: Lunch & Teatime
Sunday: Teatime & Evening

Online: bbc.co.uk/tees

* Subject to download restrictions and availability

The UK Sail Training fleet....
bringing the adventure to you

With over fifty vessels, from stately square-rigged ships to powerful round-the-world yachts, there is sure to be a vessel that captures your heart and imagination.

www.uksailtraining.co.uk

Many of the vessels in The Tall Ships Races are from the UK Sail Training family, and offer sailing adventures all year round. To discover how easy it is to take part, visit the UK Sail Training stand in the Wind Zone.

So, what are you waiting for?

ASTO Promoting UK Sail Training

a founder member of Sail Training International

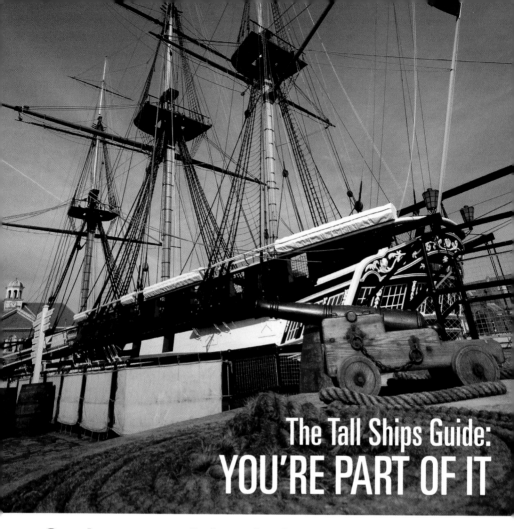

The Tall Ships Guide:
YOU'RE PART OF IT

Getting around the site!

Congratulations and welcome. It's official, you are now part of England's biggest free event, The Tall Ships Races - Hartlepool 2010.

We want to make sure you make the most of your time with us and don't miss out on any of the activities and entertainment we've got on offer. To navigate around the site and make the most of your visit the useful maps at the back of the guide will be your essential companion.

To make sure your visit is safe and comfortable we have provided public conveniences all around the site and the approaches. As well as toilets you will find changing areas for children and adults, and wheelchair accessible facilities. The whole of the site is almost completely flat, although the ground within The Tall Ships Village may be a little uneven in places.

The site has been developed with you in mind. There will be information signs throughout the site. In key locations we have created huge site plans that are there to help you find your bearings and reach your desired destination.

There are seven key Tourist Information points, each staffed by people with an expert knowledge of the local area, the site and the event programme and these points will be clearly signposted. However, if you don't know where your nearest Information Point is, you can always seek assistance from any of our Event Stewards (identifiable by their yellow jackets) or one of our Events Team in their red or yellow polo shirts.

The Tall Ships site is pedestrianised as vehicle access is restricted for your safety. Essentially, to travel right around the site from Hartlepool's Maritime Experience, up to Navigation Point and across to the A-Class Ships in the Wind Zone of The Tall Ships Village should take approximately 20-30 minutes depending upon the level of crowds and how many times you stop to take photos of this spectacular event.

If you are new to Hartlepool it's worth making a mental note of some of the fixed landmarks you can see. Start with Hartlepool's Maritime Experience where the spectacular masts of HMS Trincomalee have transformed the town's skyline. Across the water Navigation Point is Hartlepool's biggest building and home to a number of wine-bars and great restaurants. You will also find sculptures of the Hartlepool Monkey Legend and a Stag high on a plinth. Once on Navigation Point and facing the sea, look to your left for the large blue and yellow cranes, these are situated in Victoria Harbour and represent the furthest distance you need to travel to see the A-class vessels. The cranes may at this point share the vista with the masts of the tallest ships in the fleet but you can count on them not to move! So, if you're confident you now know the three fixed landmarks: Hartlepool's Maritime Experience, Navigation Point and the big blue and yellow cranes in Victoria Harbour, you're ready to make the most of the celebrations!

The main area for entertainment and refreshments is in The Tall Ships Village. This part of the site is divided into three areas, each with a different theme: Earth Zone, Fire Zone and Wind Zone.

If you're walking into the site from one of the Park & Walk sites or from the drop-off points for the Park & Ride sites just follow the directional signage. This will lead you on the safest and most convenient route to the Tall Ships. And when you need to return to your coach or car the signs will guide you safely back again.

Once you have made your way to where the largest ships, the A-Class vessels, are berthed in the Wind Zone of The Tall Ships Village, there are a couple of things to note. Across the water from the ships' berths you should be able to see a part of Hartlepool known as the Headland or 'Old' Hartlepool. You'll recognise it by the impressive Town Wall which has its foundations at the beach and by the mighty church of St Hilda's rising up from behind.

The Headland is playing its part in the celebrations as well: the annual Headland Carnival and Town Moor Fair, the official Tall Ships Fair, will be running at the same time. Also on the Headland you will find the new Town Square which will play host to the exciting Folk Festival. The Headland can be accessed by foot from the Wind Zone. The Town Moor Fair is approximately 15 minutes walk from there.

One last thing to point out is that the lock-gates at the head of the Marina will remain closed to the public during the course of The Tall Ships Races. This decision has been taken to avoid any risk of injury to any of our visitors.

So, you've got the guide, you know the landmarks to look out for and you know that there are plenty of staff to assist you with any queries. All that's left is for you to enjoy yourself and make sure you take plenty of pictures to remember this spectacular event. Enjoy!

A few things worth pointing out, and not to be missed include:

- Two hospitality tents provided by The Black Sheep Brewery in The Tall Ships Village

- The Main Stage – the place to catch all the big name acts as well as the prize-giving ceremony

- The World Market, filled with a mix of high class foods and crafts from around the world

- Meet the Georgians at Hartlepool's Maritime Experience – three days of Regency flair!

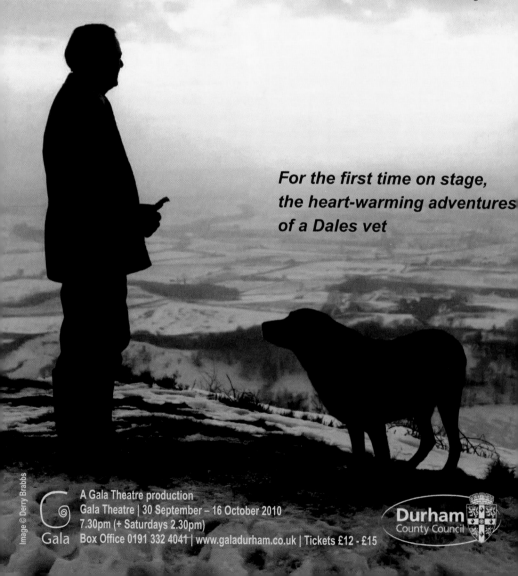

James Herriot's

All Creatures Great & Small

Adapted for the stage by Simon Stallworthy

For the first time on stage, the heart-warming adventures of a Dales vet

Image © Derry Brabbs

Gala

A Gala Theatre production
Gala Theatre | 30 September – 16 October 2010
7.30pm (+ Saturdays 2.30pm)
Box Office 0191 332 4041 | www.galadurham.co.uk | Tickets £12 - £15

Durham
County Council

Tall Ships Event Programme Everyday Events

Fireworks

Time: 9.45pm – 10.00pm
7th, 8th & 9th August

Enjoy three nights of spectacular fireworks, expertly delivered by our 'Official Fireworks Sponsor' G2 Fireworks. Everybody's favourite, the exciting displays will be fired from the South Pier and can be watched by

all from The Tall Ships Village, Headland Promenade and Seaton Promenade. With three nightly shows you don't need to miss out!

Headland Town Moor Fair

Time: 12 noon – 9.45pm
27th July - 10th August

Enjoy the traditions of the Town Moor Fair, the 'Official Tall Ships Fair'. As well as the usual thrills and spills to excite and entertain, a 42m diameter giant wheel will be taking centre stage at the fair along with 'Megatower', an impressive new ride on its first visit to Hartlepool.

Town Centre

Fighting Ships

(Saturday 19th June – Saturday 28th August)
Time: 10.00am – 5.00pm
Tuesday – Saturday
(during The Tall Ships Races event,
10.00am – 7.00pm,
Tuesday 10th – 5.00pm)
Hartlepool Art Gallery

To mark the coming of The Tall Ships Races and the Georgian celebrations at Hartlepool's Maritime Experience, the exhibition will focus on the depiction of fighting ships during the reign of George III. Split into two themes the exhibition will look at British naval power at the height of this period and the emergence of a distinctive national style of marine painting.

'After Trafalgar' by Frank Henry Mason.
Image courtesy of Laing Art Gallery,
Tyne & Wear Archives & Museums

Middleton Grange Shopping Centre

Time: 9.00am – 6.00pm
(Sunday 8th 10.30 – 4.30)
Saturday 7th – Tuesday 10th

Middleton Grange will be running a FREE shuttle bus service to the Shopping Centre from the Old Cemetery Road, at the entrance to the Headland. On selected journeys there will be a number of Middleton Grange gift cards throughout the vehicle, so everyone is in with a chance to be a lucky winner!

We will also be hosting some fantastic activities in the shopping centre, including children's face painting, a balloon modeller, the chance to meet and have your photo taken with the legendary Jack Sparrow (Saturday only) and to ride our FREE surf simulator!

Railway Artwork
Hartlepool Railway Station
The artwork for these posters was developed by Ken Dunn from photographs he had taken of the Headland area, Seaton Carew, Marina and a view from the top of Christ Church Tower. The posters are based on the Art Deco style of 1930s, 40s and 50s - this movement comprised a mix of decorative styles, including simplification, distortion, abstraction and the use of intense colours. Three of the posters have been designed in a composite style, consisting of a number of well known landmarks, arranged together to form an imaginative composition.

The Tall Ships Village

World Market
Time: 10.00am – 10.00pm
Sat 7th – Tues 10th August
Earth & Wind Zones
Enjoy 600 metres of a spectacular World Market with choices galore of food

and drink, crafts, clothing, jewellery and accessories. The organisers will draw together a number of elements – providing colour and character, blending exotic and sustainable, offering eco-friendly, original and creative.

Street Theatre Programme
Time: 12 noon – 6.00pm
7th – 10th August
walkabout
Let's Circus are a pioneering circus arts outreach company based in Newcastle. They have created six new roaming street theatre acts for Hartlepool's Tall Ships Races that will bring a colourful and playful element to the event. This world premiere of locally grown street theatre will be performed by young performance artists from across the district. Look out for their roaming characters throughout the festival

site including quirky Coral Gardeners, languid Starfish Workmen, beautiful Jelly Ladies and charismatic Stilting Sailors.

Earth Zone
The Tall Ships Village

BBC - Bang Goes the Theory Roadshow
Time: 11.00am – 6.00pm
6th – 8th August
The BBC Roadshow is coming to the event and visitors can get hands-on with science in the Interactive Arena, catch the live Bang Goes The Theory science shows, experience Dr Yan's amazing street science, ask experts science questions and discover what is on offer in local science centres.

Hot Potato Cabaret Marquee

7th – 9th August
Time: 5.00pm – 9.45pm

Hot Potato is a fantastic new monthly comedy night at Hartlepool Town Hall Theatre featuring some of the hottest talent on the circuit right now. The good news is that we've joined up with the Hot Potato team to bring you three nights of fun-packed comedy, music and cabaret as part of the Tall Ships entertainment programme. Expect thrills, spills and belly laughs galore in the first half of the show, followed by madcap musical antics from the likes of the Wildcats of Kilkenny, and the Bagdhaddies. The aim is to create a lively busking / street-theatre vibe, where anything goes, and you can just roll up at any point in the evening to join in the fun. See you down there!

Change 4 Life Marquee

Time: 10.00am – 5.00pm
7th – 10th August

Brought to you by NHS Hartlepool, focusing on promoting healthy lifestyles. It includes yoga demos, exercise demos, a Cyber Coach, Kitchen Academy family cookery workshops, smoothie bikes and cookery demos in the Northumbria Larder Demo kitchen. Celebrity guests include Mr Motivator, Aldo Zilli and Ed Baines. Outdoor activities such as netball, basketball and rugby led by the Hartlepool Sporting Association.

Fire Zone
The Tall Ships Village

Talking Heads

Times: Vary throughout the day, 6th – 10th August
Main Stage
(Big Screen)

Hartlepool Tall Ships is capturing the imagination of millions including some of the best known names in the region and the UK – many of whom have contributed to our Talking Heads video on show in the Tall Ships Village.
You'll recognise their voices and their faces – but you will be surprised by how they make use of Hartlepool's splendid maritime resources.

Wind Zone
The Tall Ships Village

The Tall Ships

20 class A ships will be berthed here and at certain times of the day visitors can go on board to speak to the Captain and crew about life on the ocean wave.

Marina

The Tall Ships

At least 40 Tall Ships will be berthed around the Marina for visitors to admire.

Hartlepool's Maritime Experience

Home of HMS Trincomalee.

Meet The Georgians

Time: 10.00am – 7.00pm, (10th August 5.00pm)
6th – 10th August

Looking at the period 1811-1820 during the rule of Prince Regent, later George IV, Hartlepool's Maritime

Experience and our very own Tall Ship, HMS Trincomalee, are transformed into a bustling Georgian seaport filled with colour, costumes, comedy, traditional entertainment, swordfighting displays, pistol duels and much much more. Discounted admission price applies – only £2.00 per person!

A Nice Cup Of Tea! From Cosies To Clippers

Daily 10.00am – 5.00pm (during The Tall Ships Races, 10.00am – 7.00pm, 10th August 5.00pm) Saturday 24th July – Sunday 17th October Museum of Hartlepool

It is hard to believe that such a national institution as a nice cup of tea had not been heard of in Britain before the 1660s. Find out about the cultivation of tea, how it came to Britain and the rituals that have developed around its making and drinking.

Date specific events

Saturday 31st July

Behold, the Sea! Cleveland Philharmonic Orchestra

Time: 7.30pm Borough Hall
The Mowbray Orchestra and the Cleveland Philharmonic Choir present Behold the Sea! A Concert for The Tall Ships Races 2010. The programme opens with atmospheric orchestra music evocative of England's North Sea and its coastal communities – the Sea Interludes from Benjamin Britten's opera Peter Grimes. This is followed by Elgar's Sea Pictures, a group of songs about the sea in all its moods. Anna Stéphany, the mezzo-soprano soloist, has appeared several times at the Proms and represented England in the 2009 BBC Cardiff Singer of the World. The second half of the programme is devoted to one work – A Sea Symphony by Ralph Vaughan Williams, with soloists Madeleine Pierard and Dawid Kimberg.
Tickets on Sale: 01429 890000

Wednesday 4th August

The Beacon of Welcome

Time: 8.30pm – 9.45pm (approximately)
Seaton Carew Beach
This event signifies the 5 Boroughs of Tees Valley coming together to welcome The Tall Ships Races to Tees Valley. Enjoy folk, entertainment and storytelling as a beacon is lit to signal the ships coming to Hartlepool.

Friday 6th August

Local & Regional Band Programme

Time: 5.15pm till 22:30pm

Arcs & Trauma

Time: 5.15pm – 5.45pm

A local band who whilst having the difficult task of opening proceedings on a busy night in the bustling White Room, stole the show from their older more experienced counterparts. Having already established a loyal following thanks to their online presence, they bring a punchy brand of contemporary rock and indie pop.

Runwells

Time: 6.05pm – 6.40pm
A four piece band from Newcastle who turn their hands to zesty indie-rock with plenty of oomph. The Runwells are very much an energetic live band and they often invite guest musicians on stage. Variety is definitely the spice of life with additional instruments including steel pan, flute, e-cello, sax, keys and violin.

Antlez

Time: 7.00pm – 7.35pm

Hartlepool's very own indie popstars. With their at times military drumbeat, underscored by a spiky and exciting performance, the group divide their attention on stage between their guitars and their audience.

The Standards

Time: 7.55pm – 8.30pm

This twitchy, highly addictive London trio have been around the city's dustier haunts for a few years, but now have a debut single 'Out of the Fire' finally launched. They write good music, structure it into something modern, lavish with kitsch guitars and package it in a way which is fresh.

The White Negroes

Time: 8.50pm – 9.25pm

With their bacchanal beats, shamanistic live performances and philosophy of recreational hedonism, The White Negroes are quite simply the last, great British rock'n'roll band. These 21st century hipsters bring to Hartlepool hands-in-the-air club rock anthems.

Dirty Weekend

Time: 9.45pm – 10.30pm

Dirty Weekend have been described as powerful, adventurous, and quirky. Their music is punchy and brave, eclectic inspired pop with distinctly darker undertones.

Carnival Arts Workshops

Time: 10.00am – 1.30pm

Headland Town Square

Carnival Artists will run workshops which will include mask making, face painting and structure making.

Headland Carnival

Time: All Day, Headland

Enjoy a host of activities and spectacles at the Carnival including St. Hilda's Church lunches (all day), Nutty Slack Derby (2.00pm) and Parade Judging (3pm). This will be followed at 4pm by the Carnival Parade, featuring a mix of colourful costumes and entertainment parading around the heart of the Headland.

Opening Ceremony

Time: 12.00 noon – 12.30pm

The Tall Ships Village – Fire Zone, Main Stage

The Official opening of The Tall Ships Races starts appropriately with cannon fire from Hartlepool's Maritime Experience followed by an official opening speech and welcome by the Mayor of Hartlepool.

Roots & Folk Music Programme

Time: 1:00pm – 11:30pm

The Tall Ships Village – Fire Zone, Main Stage

Cattle And Cane

Time: 1.00pm – 1.35pm

This group is a real family affair, with brother and sister Joe and Helen originally starting out as a duo performing around the local area, eventually enlisting brother Frank on Bass and Paul Wilson on drums.

Dave Moseley Band

Time: 2.00pm – 2.35pm

Made up of members of Moses and Mercedes, the group's sound is a gritty mixture of Bob Dylan, Kings of Leon, Creedence Clearwater Revival and Yes Yes Give Me Your Jam Jars.

The Woven Project

Time: 3.05pm – 3.45pm

Formed in early 2009, Hartlepool musicians collective, The Woven Project are lo-fi, acoustic and experimental with a folk influence, bringing you melancholic, soulful music from the heart.

Sheelanagig

Time: 4.15pm – 4.55pm

Sheelanagig have been honing their eclectic blend of folk, jazz and world music since early 2005. Equally at home on festival stages, music venues and street corners, the band have developed a devoted following with two album releases and a hectic touring schedule.

Stornoway

Time: 5.25pm – 6.15pm

Named after the Hebridean island , but hailing from Oxford, Stornoway are a four piece band of songsmiths, scholars, scientists and men of the earth. Their charming brand of quintessential pop, steeped in pastoral hues, won them fans across press and radio.

CW Stoneking

Time: 6.45pm – 7.45pm

A musician who draws influence from pre-war blues, jazz, 1920s calypso, folklore and personal experience to produce his unique original songs. Stoneking's songs range in style from lonesome field holler blues, to hokum

blues duets, to full blown jungle epics.

The Unthanks

Time: 8.20pm – 9.30pm

The Unthanks are described by Ian MacMillan as the 'inheritors, curators and gleeful distorters' of Tyneside traditions. They draw on elements of blues, jazz, music hall, burlesque cabaret, classical and leftfield contemporary music for their folk music. Winner of the Horizon Award at the BBC Folk Awards in 2008.

Seth Lakeman

Time: 10.10pm – 11.30pm

Mercury Music Prize nominated Seth Lakeman's 2006 album sold over 100,000 copies in the UK alone and helped build his traditional cult following,

finding a new audience for his rhythmic, captivating brand of indie-folk songwriting.

Headland Folk Festival – Sea Stage

Time: 7.00pm -10.00pm
Headland Town Square

Mrs Trevor's Deep Freeze Secrets

Time: 7.00pm – 7.25pm
An exciting and wonderfully named 5 piece ceilidh band.

Sheelanagig

Time: 7.30pm – 8.30pm
Sheelanagig have been honing their eclectic blend of folk, jazz and world music since early 2005. Equally at home on festival stages, music venues and street corners, the band have developed a devoted following with two album releases and a hectic touring schedule.

Brasy
Time: 8.35pm – 9.05pm
Five man Polish supremos Brasy are a vocal tour de force.

The Young'Uns
Time: 9.10pm – 9.45pm
Local lads The Young'Uns have over the last few years earned a glowing reputation on the UK folk scene.

Hot Potato Cabaret Marquee
Time: 5.00pm – 9:45pm
The Tall Ships Village – Earth Zone
Enjoy a host of acts at the cabaret marquee, creating a lively bustling street theatre vibe.

Sir Thomas Allen Concert
Time: 7.30pm – 10.00pm
Town Hall Theatre
Music lovers will have the rare chance to see one of the leading lights of the

opera world in Hartlepool. Only 400 people will be able to see the internationally acclaimed baritone give a one-off recital which will include a selection of operatic pieces but also some sea shanties with a local flavour.

Fireworks
Time: 9.45pm – 10.00pm

Sunday 8th August

Church Service
11.00am – 12 noon
The Tall Ships Village – Fire Zone, Main Stage
Churches Together have brought together a service led by the Bishop of Jarrow and including a Mass Choir, Silver Band and readings.

Headland Folk Festival

Time: 10.00am – 5.00pm
Headland Town Square

Ian Glover
Time: 10am – 12.25pm
Known affectionately as the 'miserable mandolin player', Iain is a musician of great integrity.

Judith Haswell
Time: 12.30pm – 12.55pm
A voice of rare clarity, feeling and expression –

one of the stalwarts of the North East folk scene.

Four 'n' Aft
Time: 1.00pm – 1.25pm
One of the most in demand and highly regarded maritime groups in Europe.

Coracle
Time: 1.30pm – 1.55pm
Coracle focus on English traditional music with an exciting and energetic twist.

Wendy Arrowsmith & Blind Summat
Time: 2.00pm – 2.25pm
Award-winning Scottish singer songwriter with a growing reputation as a true bearer of songs.

Brasy
Time: 2.30pm – 2.55pm
Five man Polish supremos Brasy are a vocal tour de force.

Richard Grainger
Time: 3.00pm – 3.25pm
This respected globetrotting troubadour is regarded as one of the finest songwriters to come out of the North East.

Mrs Trevor's Deep Freeze Secrets
Time: 3.30pm – 3.55pm
An exciting and wonderfully named 5 piece ceilidh band.

Benny Graham
4.00pm – 4.25pm
Benny is widely regarded as one of the finest singers on the folk scene, a true voice of the North.

Marske Fishermen's Choir
4.30pm – 5.00pm
The choir has been singing and entertaining audiences while raising money for the RNLI for nearly 50 years.

Mr Motivator
Time: 12.30pm – 1.00pm
The Tall Ships Village – Earth Zone,
Change 4 Life Marquee
The TV legend will bring his exercise routines to Hartlepool and promote the benefits of healthy living.

Her Majesty's Royal Marines Band (Scotland)
Time: 1.00 – 2.00 pm
The Tall Ships Village – Fire Zone
Come and be entertained by the Royal Marines Band as they play on the Main Stage.

Carnival Crew Tees Valley
Time: 2.00pm – 3.00pm
The Tall Ships Village – Fire Zone
The Carnival Crew Tees Valley will entertain with a

performance of dance and music before starting the Crew Parade celebrations.

Crew Parade
Time: 3.00pm – 4.00pm
Various locations
A memorable marching display by representatives from every ship in the Races, often in traditional costumes or even fancy dress! Hundreds of parade participants will follow a route out of The Tall Ships Village, along Middleton Road before turning onto Marina Way, turning left and passing in front of Hartlepool's Maritime Experience and up Harbour Walk back into The Tall Ships Village. The parade will be accompanied by lively music and street theatre making this a real spectacle for all ages to enjoy.

Prize Giving Ceremony
Time: 4.00pm – 5.30pm
The Tall Ships Village – Fire Zone (Main Stage)
The prize giving ceremony will celebrate all the successful ships and their crews after a long and testing race. 14 prizes will be distributed to Captains and crew members from the winning ships, all in full view of the crowds in The Tall Ships Village.

Hot Potato Cabaret Marquee
The Tall Ships Village – Earth Zone
Time: 5.00pm 9.45pm
Enjoy a host of acts at the cabaret marquee, creating a lively bustling street theatre vibe.

Easy Listening Music Programme
Time: 5:30pm – 11:30pm
The Tall Ships Village – Fire Zone, Main Stage

Mercedes
Time: 5.30pm – 6.00pm

As founding members of Hartlepool's most successful band, Mercedes, Sharon and Mark Pinchen have toured all over Europe, supported the likes of Coldplay and played at the Leeds and Reading

Festivals. Sharon has the kind of voice that immediately evokes the sublime ornate, yet it's a humble Hartlepool soul that lends their dreamy atmospheric sound a unique charm.

Elaine Palmer
Time: 6.20pm – 7.00pm
Since the release of her first album 'Into the Spotlight', Elaine Palmer has played with a host of successful artists including James Blunt and KT Tunstall. Her fan base increased after receiving airplay on Radio 2 as well as numerous regional stations. Described as having a tough but tender voice, both sultry and intelligent, she has some great acoustic songs of her own creation.

Goldheart Assembly
Time: 7.25pm – 8.10pm
This London based band of six released their debut album 'Wolves and Thieves', winning fans everywhere with its unique blend of English psychedelia, pitch perfect harmonies and surprising twists and turns. They have built up a lively fan-base via BBC Introducing Stages at Glastonbury and Reading / Leeds.

Duke Special
Time: 8.40pm – 9.30pm
Since 2002, Duke Special has been the alter ego of Peter Wilson, a 39 year old Belfast-based musician who has brought a dash

of drama and vaudeville flair to the singer songwriter's art.

Ocean Colour Scene
Time: 10.10pm – 11.30pm

Ocean Colour Scene burst to prominence in 1996 with the release of 'Moseley Shoals' which spent 18 months in the UK charts. 'Marching Already' followed which reached No 1 in the charts, their second of five Top 10 albums. They've gone on from strength to strength in recent years, selling out UK tours and being voted best band at V Festival in 2007.

Headland Folk Festival

Time: 7:00pm - 10:30pm
Headland Town Square

Coracle
Time: 7.00pm – 7.25pm
Coracle focus on English traditional music with an exciting and energetic twist.

Wendy Arrowsmith & Blind Summat
Time: 7.30pm – 7.55pm
Award-winning Scottish singer songwriter with a

growing reputation as a true bearer of songs.

The Askew Sisters
Time: 8.00pm – 8.25pm
Young duo making waves on the folk scene with their energetic brand of English folk music.

Four 'n' Aft
Time: 8.30pm – 8.55pm
One of the most in demand and highly regarded maritime groups in Europe.

Serious Sam Barrett
Time: 9.00pm – 9.40pm
This superb bluegrass musician brings his very own brand of music to the Headland – "Yorkshirecana".

Brasy
Time: 9.45pm – 10.30pm
Five man Polish supremos Brasy are a vocal tour de force.

Monday 9th August

Popular Music Programme
Time: 1.00pm – 11.30pm
The Tall Ships Village – Fire Zone, Main Stage

Atlantic in Transit
Time: 1.00pm – 1.30pm
A Hartlepool group whose sounds blend together the guitar tapping of Minus the Beat with the raw edge of Pretty Gils Makes Graves.

Up! Down! Strange
Time: 1.50pm – 2.20pm

A Hartlepool band who have reached an uncompromising crossroads of synth and chiming guitars, complex math rock and ska rhythms with psychedelic soul.

Lost State of Dance
Time: 2.40pm – 3.10pm
Providing a dynamic mature sound that will get you wanting to hear more, Lost State of Dance provide a mix of electro synth guitar based, pop indie dance. The infectious music and lyrical hooks will keep people enthused.

Demon Summer
Time: 3.30pm – 4.10pm
The band have toured exclusively around the UK, touring venues and festivals and supporting bands such as Long-View, Block Party, Leaves, Maximo Park and Hope of the States.

Chased By Wolves
Time: 4.30pm – 5.15pm
This Newcastle five piece blends blues, country and alt-folk into a gorgeous melting pot that evokes artists as varied as Bob Dylan, Fleetwood Mac and Ryan Adams. However the band are not simply pretenders - they are definitely amongst the big players, inhabiting a musical space that is all their own.

Sparrow And The Workshop
Time: 5.45pm – 6.30pm

From a tiny top floor flat in SE Glasgow, Belfast born, Chicago raised Jill O'Sullivan, Welshman Nick Packer and Scottish drummer Gregor Donaldson have carved themselves a unique niche in contemporary music that somehow manages to traverse and blur any number of geographic and musical boundaries with stunning effect.

Exit Calm
Time: 7.00pm – 7.45pm
South Yorkshire's four piece Exit Calm provides ragged vocals and swathes of widescreen guitar effects, reminiscent of early Verve.

Echo and The Bunnymen
Time: 8.20pm – 9.30pm

Liverpool's finest indie-rock legends Echo and The Bunnymen – expect all the classic hits including 'The Cutter', 'Nothing lasts Forever' and 'The Killing Moon' from these iconic legends, as well as a quality back catalogue spanning over 30 years.

Doves
Time: 10.10pm – 11.30pm
Manchester's indie-rock heroes will headline the Entertainment Stage. Their greatest hits album 'The Places Between' celebrates 12 years at the top of the UK music charts. With two Number One albums and last year's 'Kingdom of Rust' hitting the next best spot, fans can expect to hear the hits 'There Goes the Fear', 'Black and White Town' , 'Pounding' and a host of others.

Never Knowingly Undersold is our lifelong commitment to provide excellent service, like our free five year guarantee on all our TVs.

Never Knowingly Undersold
on quality | on price | on service

FIVE BUSINESS AREAS
ONE PORT OF TYNE

CONVENTIONAL & BULK CARGO | CAR TERMINALS | CRUISE & FERRIES | LOGISTICS | ESTATES

Maritime House, Tyne Dock, South Shields, Tyne & Wear NE34 9PT
Tel: +44 191 455 2671 Fax: +44 191 455 4687

www.portoftyne.co.uk

Creating a vibrant, sustainable Port of Tyne

Whilst the Port of Tyne's heritage can be traced back through several centuries, it is the vision and radical investment by its Board and management team that is creating a vibrant, sustainable working port for the future.

The triple values of customer focus, people focus and long term thinking, together with a programme to ensure resources are used to their maximum efficiency and valuable infrastructure is developed and maintained and fit for purpose, enables the port to keep pace with the ever-changing markets and requirements of its customers.

That the port is a major asset to the region is beyond question. Its five commercial business areas – bulk & conventional cargo, car terminals, cruise & ferries, logistics, and estates; three rail terminals and a modern international cruise and passenger terminal bringing tourists contributing to the local economy – all add value to North East England. And its Marine Services undertake the statutory responsibilities for conservancy and the safety of all navigation on the 23 miles of the tidal reach of the river Tyne.

Traditionally famous for its coal exports, the radical changes in the UK's mining industry during the 1990s created an urgent need for the port to diversify to remain viable. And while the port has successfully entered into new markets, ranging from car exports, imports and trans-shipments, through to logistics and cruise and ferries, helping the port earn the accolade of European Port of the Year for three consecutive years, and one of the finalists in the Seatrade Insider Cruise Port of the Year 2008, energy is once again holding pole position in the port's portfolio; it was ranked the fourth largest importer of coal in the UK in 2008.

And the future? Recent exciting opportunities include the announcement by MGT Power of their plan, subject to planning approval, to build their biomass-fuelled Tyne Renewable Energy plant on the port's north bank at North Shields. That creative thinking and partnership working can provide solutions that are both environmentally sound and cost effective has been borne out with the creation of 13 acres of much needed operational land on the south bank of the river at South Shields by infilling the port's Tyne Dock with the spoil from the construction of the second Tyne Tunnel. 2009 ended on a high-note with the signing of an agreement between the Port of Tyne and Drax Power Limited for the provision of handling and covered storage facilities for between 0.5 million and 1.4 million tonnes of biomass per annum, for an initial 10 year period on the port's south bank at South Shields. Both projects contributing significantly to North East England's growing role at the forefront of the low-carbon economy.

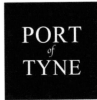

PORT
of
TYNE

Hot Potato Cabaret Marquee

Time 5.00pm - 9.45pm
The Tall Ships Village –
Earth Zone
Enjoy a host of acts at the
cabaret marquee, creating a
lively bustling street
theatre vibe.

Headland Folk Festival

Time: 2.00pm – 10.00pm
Headland Town Square

The Keelers

Time: 2.00pm – 2.25pm
Formed for the 1986
Newcastle Tall Ships Races
The Keelers have performed
at many of The Tall Ships
Races events over the past
24 years.

Wendy Arrowsmith

Time: 2.30pm – 2.55pm
An award winning Scottish
singer songwriter with a
growing reputation as a
true bearer of songs.

The Askew Sisters

Time: 3.00pm – 3.25pm
Young duo making waves
on the folk scene with
their energetic brand
of English folk music.

Dogwatch

Time: 3.30pm – 3.55pm
Singing songs fit to grace the
foc'sle of any Tall Ship.

Serious Sam Barrett

Time: 4.00pm – 4.25pm
This superb bluegrass

musician brings his very own
brand of music to the
Headland – "Yorkshirecana".

Four 'n' Aft

Time: 4.30pm – 4.55pm
One of the most in demand
and highly regarded maritime
groups in Europe.

Coracle

Time: 5.00pm - 5.25pm
Coracle focus on English
traditional music with
an exciting and
energetic twist.

Benny Graham

Time: 5.30pm – 5.55pm
Widely regarded as one
of the finest singers on
the folk scene, a true
voice of the North.

Richard Grainger & the Endeavour Shantymen

Time: 6.00 – 6.25pm
This respected globetrotting
troubadour is regarded as one
of the finest songwriters to
come out of the North East.

Ian Mckone

Time: 6.30pm – 6.55pm
One of the finest young folk
musicians around, with a
voice hewn straight from the
Durham collieries.

The Young'Uns

Time: 7.00pm – 7.25pm
Local lads the Young'Uns have
over the last few years earned
a glowing reputation on the
UK folk scene.

Mrs Trevor's Deep Freeze Secrets

Time: 7.30pm – 7.55pm
An exciting and
wonderfully named
5 piece ceilidh band.

Brasy

Time: 8.00pm – 8.35pm
Five man Polish supremos
Brasy are a vocal tour de force.

Steve Percival

Time: 8.40pm – 8.45pm
'Song for the Sea'
competition winner!

Jez Lowe

Time: 8.50pm – 9.45pm
Richard Thompson called
Lowe "the best songwriter
to emerge from the UK in
a long time".

Tuesday 10th August

World Music Programme:

Time: 11.00am – 6.00pm

Ali and The Beachcombers

Time: 12.00 noon – 12.45pm
5.00pm – 6.00pm

Scarborough based 7 piece Ali
and The Beachcombers play
a mix of their own material
and a host of classic Reggae
covers!

Middlesbrough Jazz & Blues Orchestra

Time: 1.10pm – 2.00pm
Founded in 2005 by leading
Jazz trombonist Andrew

Kerensky, MJBO have required a reputation as one of Tees Valley's outstanding big bands. A community based band they play a range of music in the tradition of great swing bands – from Jazz, Jive, Gospel and Soul to Latin, Funk, Be-bop and Blues.

Rhythms of Samba
Time: 2.20 noon – 3.20pm
The energetic and sizzling samba rhythms of Brazilian-style loud and infectious street-music are brought to life by this stunning samba band.

Gypsy Swing Band
Time: 3.40 noon – 4.40pm
The Gypsy Swing Trio presents a tribute to the music of the late, great Stephane Grappelli and Django Rheinhardt. From frenetic full on swing jazz to atmospheric and soulful Tangos and Gypsy tunes, this is Exciting, Exotic and Dynamic stuff at it's best!

Headland Folk Festival

Time: 2.00pm – 5.30pm
Headland Town Square

Rebekah Findlay
Time: 2.00pm – 2.25pm
An emerging song writing talent from North Yorkshire.

The Keelers
Time: 2.30pm – 2.55pm
Formed for the 1986 Newcastle Tall Ships Races The Keelers have performed at many of The Tall Ships Races events over the past 24 years.

Mrs Trevor's Deep Freeze Secrets
Time: 3.00pm – 3.25pm
An exciting and wonderfully named 5 piece ceilidh band.

Ian McKone
Time: 3.30pm – 3.55pm
One of the finest young folk musicians around, with a voice hewn straight from the Durham collieries.

The Young'Uns
Time: 4.00pm – 4.25pm
Local lads the Young'Uns have over the last few years earned a glowing reputation on the UK folk scene.

Brasy
Time: 4.30pm – 4.55pm
Five man Polish supremos Brasy are a vocal tour de force.

Four 'n' Aft
Time: 5.00pm – 5.30pm
One of the most in demand and highly regarded maritime groups in Europe.

The Grand Farewell – Parade of Sail
2.00pm – 7.00pm

The Grand Farewell / Parade of Sail will provide a dramatic finale to The Tall Ships Races. The ships will leave their berths at the Marina and Port, proceed out into Hartlepool Bay, form into the parade and sail past Hartlepool as a final farewell.
The first ships should leave the Marina around 1pm. These will hold in an area off Seaton Carew. By shortly after 3pm the largest vessels will be departing and these will sail past Seaton Carew towards the Tees first before they turn to the north-west and the Parade of Sail commences at 4pm. The Parade route will take the ships past Hartlepool towards the Headland and then along the coast to Blackhalls Point. Ships will continue to depart from the port and the Marina until around 5.30pm, creating a spectacular display. The Parade of Sail will end as the final ships pass Blackhalls Point around 7pm.

Wednesday 11th August

North Sea Tall Ships Regatta:
Estimated time of start: 1.00pm
Start of the race from Hartlepool to IJmuiden – further details on page 133.

TRAVEL & TRANSPORT

PARKING
The best place to park your car is in the Park & Ride and Park & Walk sites. At least 26,000 car park spaces are available each day at the 6 designated sites.

PARK & RIDE
- Off the A179 near Hart
- Off the A689 at Greatham
- Corus in Brenda Road (South Hartlepool)

PARK & WALK
- Coronation Drive (Seaton Carew)
- Oakesway Trading Estate (off A179)
- Central Park (off West View Road)

Frequent shuttles will take you from the Park & Ride sites directly to the event with drop off points in Greenland Road for buses from the north of the town and the new Transport Interchange for buses from the south.

Park & Walk sites are located a 15-20 minute walk from the main site.

CHARGES
Park & Ride - £10.00 on the day, £7.50 if pre-booked in advance online or by telephone
Inclusive of parking and free travel for all vehicle passengers
Park & Walk - £10.00 on the day

OPENING TIMES
Park & Ride sites are open at 8.00am with first buses to take people to site at 9.00am and close at 1.00am each night.

CYCLING
A secure site is available off Greenland Road. There is no charge for cycles. A wristband security system will be in operation to identify owners when they return to collect their cycles.

CYCLE ROUTES
Hartlepool and the Tall Ships site can be accessed by the recognised National Route 14 which is part of the National Cycle Network. National Route 14 links Hartlepool to Peterlee to the North and Stockton and the rest of Tees Valley to the South. To the North the route can be joined with National Route 1 for safer cycling routes to Durham and Tyne and Wear. Several bespoke routes into The Tall Ships Village have been plotted on the Tees Valley Cycling Website: www.doitbycycle.com which is co-ordinated by www.sustrans.org.uk.

BLUE BADGE PARKING
500 parking spaces have been allocated for Blue Badge parking on Greenland Road, near to The Tall Ships Village. Spaces can be pre-booked online, by telephone or by dropping into Hartlepool Contact Centre, for £7.50 per car per day.

MOTORCYCLES
A secure site is available for 500 motorcycles off Greenland Road. Cost is £5 per day.

ROAD CLOSURES
Some roads around the Tall Ships site will be closed in the interests of safety. **These include: Marina Way**, between the ASDA roundabout and Buoy roundabout (Middleton Road), closed from 1pm to midnight on 7, 8, 9 and 10 August. **Maritime Avenue** (between Marina Way and Victoria Terrace) and **Middleton Road** will both be closed from 9.00am until approximately midnight on 6,7,8,9 and 10 August. **Coronation Drive**, Seaton Carew, will be closed to through traffic for the Parade of Sail from 2.00pm to 9.00pm on Tuesday 10 August. Access to and from the Park and Walk site will be maintained.

The Lock Gates in the Marine will be closed 6 - 10 August for pedestrians.

For regular traffic updates throughout the Tall Ships event listen to BBC Tees on 95FM.

TRAIN SERVICES

Hartlepool Council has linked up with train operators to put on extra carriages to existing trains plus some late services. Plans include:

• The current Northern Rail service running to timetable with additional carriages between 7am and 9.20pm.

• Grand Central will run a normal service but an extra two trains will run from Sunderland to York between 10pm and 11.30pm.

• There will be additional hourly shuttle services between 8am and midnight from Sunderland to Darlington calling only at Hartlepool. Exact timings for this service are still to be confirmed.

Please check timetables for these additional services and any other public transport information, visit www.connectteesvalley.com

BUS SERVICES

Owing to some road closures in Hartlepool, certain buses will be re-routed. Principally the Service 7 from the Fens to the Headland (and vice-versa) and Service 527 will be re-routed. Buses will aim to run to timetable as far as possible, but there will obviously be a significantly increased volume of traffic on the roads. For further public transport information, visit www.connectteesvalley.com

MIDDLETON GRANGE SHUTTLE BUS

Middleton Grange will be running a FREE shuttle bus from the Old Cemetery Road (at the entrance to the Headland) to the Shopping Centre at Victoria Road (near the War Memorial). On selected journeys there will be a number of Middleton Grange gift cards throughout the vehicle, so everyone is in with a chance to be a lucky winner!

TAXIS

Taxi ranks will be provided for the duration of the event at Old Cemetery Road and at the Transport Interchange in Church Street.

AT A GLANCE CONTACT DETAILS
By telephone: 01429 523636
In person: Contact Centre, Civic Centre
Pre-book online:
www.hartlepooltallships2010.com

USEFUL WEBSITES
www.hartlepooltallships2010.com
www.connectteesvalley.com
www.doitbycycle.com
www.grandcentralrail.co.uk
www.northernrail.org

THE Rib Room
STEAKHOUSE & GRILL

HARDWICK HALL HOTEL
SEDGEFIELD • CO DURHAM • TS21 2EH

OPENING JULY 2010

RAISING THE STEAKS AT HARDWICK HALL!

HARDWICK HALL
HOTEL

Inspirational Hartlepool

Host port of The Tall Ships Races 2010

Over the following pages are just a few images to savour of Hartlepool.
Share in these sights when you visit to view the majestic masts of the Tall Ships
or at another time when you return after the ships have moved on but the views,
the landscape and the character endures.

"Clear blue skies, white foamy waves crashing against
the rocky coastline, the sun glinting on rockpools, boats
bobbing out to sea in the distance, the wind blowing
the cobwebs away and salty seaspray on your lips.
That's my picture of the hidden gem that is Hartlepool's
historic Headland coastline and the place that makes
Hartlepool special in my eyes."

Michelle Daurat
Tall Ships Project Manager – Hartlepool 2010
Hartlepool Borough Council

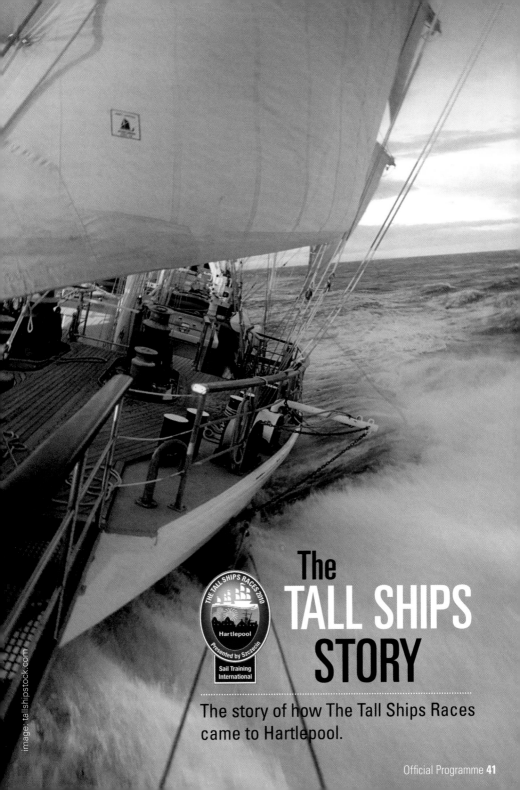

image: tallshipstock.com

The
TALL SHIPS
STORY

The story of how The Tall Ships Races
came to Hartlepool.

Hartlepool's relationship with big events started in 2000 with the Millennium Festival. Back then an estimated crowd of more than 70,000 visitors made their way to Hartlepool Marina for a weekend of live music, street theatre and a celebration of all things maritime. That was just the start – and what a start! Following the success of the Millennium Festival it was agreed that a 'maritime festival' should be planned for Hartlepool every two years. In 2002 the plans and shape of the festival became even more ambitious, and as a result, even better attended.

In 2004 the festival suffered from the rigours of the great British weather but the hardy visitors didn't let this dampen their spirits or resolve. This year also marked Hartlepool's first ever encounter with The Tall Ships Races. The Captain of the HM Bark Endeavour, a full scale replica of Captain Cook's most famous ship, made a tentative enquiry about visiting Hartlepool in the summer. After a rewarding site visit the Captain, Chris Blake, made the decision to come to Hartlepool to enhance the planned Maritime Festival. To make things even better Captain Blake mentioned this trip to his friend Vladimir Martous, the Captain of the Tall Ship STS Shtandart, and suggested that he set his compass for Hartlepool over the same weekend.

So, in the first weekend of July 2004 Hartlepool welcomed both HM Bark Endeavour and STS Shtandart to herald the start of that particular Maritime Festival. This was marked by the first ever mock battle of its type in British waters by two such ships! This spectacle was incredibly well received and the true pinnacle of that year's festival. It certainly left Hartlepool hungry for more, and thankfully the wait wasn't too long…

almost totally inaccessible with dangerous sea conditions at the outer harbour denying safe entry. Fortunately for Hartlepool, entry to its deep-water Victoria Harbour and award-winning Marina were still a safe option for Captains seeking friendly refuge for their weary crew.

So, in the early hours of the 24th July, the first of the exhausted fleet of Tall Ships crept silently into Hartlepool. By the end of the day a handful of vessels had sought shelter in the Marina and the deep waters of Victoria Harbour. And then the story of the giant ships reached the newsrooms of the local media and by teatime teams of reporters and camera crew had come to see for themselves. Once broadcast on local news channels and splashed across the pages of the regional press the public suddenly became aware of this organic, ad-hoc, Tall Ships event occurring in Hartlepool.

As Thursday turned into Friday the fleet of ships grew again: mighty vessels such as the Alexander Von Humboldt and the Christian Radich rubbed shoulders with smaller ships such as Ocean Scout, Queen Galadriel and Swan. The party vessel Mercedes proved a popular watering hole for visitors and crew alike! As the body of vessels increased, so did the number of visitors. By Saturday a supporting entertainment programme was in full swing! A music stage showcased the very best in local talent. A community stage offered a platform for local groups to wow whole new audiences. Some of the favourite street-theatre performers from previous festivals returned to delight and confuse the public in equal measures.

After a taste of the Tall Ships the events team at Hartlepool were alerted to the planned events for 2005. With The Tall Ships Races due to return to the banks of NewcastleGateshead for the third time, an opportunity was identified. The fleet of ships, 84 in total, were contractually obliged to take their place on the River Tyne on 25th July at noon. This meant that a number of ships would be looking to other ports on the North East coast for berths in the days leading up to this. What an opportunity!

The team from Hartlepool proactively contacted all of the fleet, paying particular attention to the Captains of the A-class vessels, suggesting that a short sojourn in Hartlepool would be ideal. Hartlepool was not alone in making plans for such an opportunity – other ports including Middlesbrough, Whitby and Sunderland all had aspirations to welcome a mini-fleet to their berths.

However, good planning accounts for most eventualities, but nothing can allow for the British weather! As ships made their way along the North East coastline the weather took a marked turn for the worst. The port of Whitby became

To help the impromptu event run smoothly a small band of volunteer Ship Liaison Officers were recruited to assist with the needs of the ships and their crews. The public demand to see the Tall Ships was unparalleled, and the event team assembled from Hartlepool Borough Council and its partners in Hartlepool Marina Ltd and PD Ports Ltd rose to the challenge. Traffic control measures were implemented and adjusted as the event grew and grew.

Sunday afternoon arrived and the ships prepared themselves for the short journey to the NewcastleGateshead riverbanks. As the day, and the festival, drew to a close the last of the Tall Ships slipped through the lock-gates to a round of cheers and some tears as well. In total, 37 of these magnificent vessels visited Hartlepool's waters and an astonishing 175,000 visitors came to witness them!

At the end of the racing season there is an annual conference offering Tall Ships' captains and owners the opportunity to give feedback on the year's races. These meetings consider all the features and benefits of the Official Host Ports that have been visited through the year. At the conference the name of a particular 'unofficial' port kept cropping up, that port was of course Hartlepool.

'Captains reported about the warmth of the welcome they received – each visiting ship was met at sea, day or night, and presented with a case of Cameron's 'Strongarm' beer as part of their special 'Hartlepool welcome'

Many ships reported the extraordinary lengths that the organisers went to in terms of support. For example, the vessel Lord Rank lost its propeller in its final drive into Victoria Harbour. This was a potentially race-ending scenario for the ship and its crew, however, within 24 hours a new propeller had been sourced and bespoke locking-nuts were manufactured in-situ to enable the ship to remain in the competition. Special praise was also given to the volunteer Ship Liaison Officers who never flagged in their mission to help the crews, each bringing a wealth of expert local knowledge with them.

Following this feedback the port and town of Hartlepool was invited to bid for the prestigious status of becoming a Host Port for the Races in 2010, then some years off. With just a handful of weeks to do it, a professional and personal bid was hand-delivered to the offices of Sail Training International.

After waiting for weeks, which felt like years, the message finally came back from Sail Training International – and on 28th June 2006 Hartlepool learned that it had been successful in its bid and was to be the destination Host Port for The Tall Ships Races 2010! The news that The Tall Ships Races were coming back to the North East was amazing and for Hartlepool it meant that the hard work started straight away! Now all that endeavour is coming together and the town and people of Hartlepool are waiting to do what they do best – host a great event with a huge welcome.

HARDWICK HALL
HOTEL
SEDGEFIELD . CO. DURHAM . TS21 2EH

IF YOU ARE LOOKING FOR A PREMIER EVENT WITH GOURMET FOOD, UNLIMITED SELECTED BEVERAGES, EXCELLENT LIVE ENTERTAINMENT WITH LAUGHTER AND DANCING, THIS WILL BE THE EVENT FOR ANY CORPORATE OR PRIVATE GATHERING.

THE SEVENTH NORTH EAST
OYSTER FESTIVAL

▮ FRIDAY 10ᵀᴴ SEPTEMBER 2010 ▮

BRADLEY WALSH

THE WILD CATS OF KILKENNY
THE UNTOUCHABLES   MCALPINE FUSILIERS
JJ GALWAY BAND   COMPERED BY STEVE WALLS

TICKETS: £130.00 + VAT PER PERSON / £1300.00 + VAT PER TABLE
INCLUSIVE OF: CHAMPAGNE RECEPTION
FREE FLOWING GUINNESS ALL DAY
FREE FLOWING JOHN SMITH'S & FOSTERS LAGER ALL DAY
COMPLIMENTARY BOTTLE OF WINE PER PERSON
FANTASTIC FRUITS DE MER PER TABLE
LOBSTER, CRAB, DUBLIN BAY PRAWNS, POACHED SALMON & MUSSELS, ETC
ALSO, NUMEROUS OYSTER STALLS
GIANT STRAWBERRY PAVLOVAS AND CHEESE & BISCUITS

11.30AM RECEPTION. CARRIAGES AT 6PM.
STRICT DRESS CODE - GENTLEMAN SUIT AND TIE. LADIES COCKTAIL DRESS AND HAT.

PLEASE DRINK RESPONSIBLY

PLEASE CONTACT THE EVENTS TEAM ON:
TEL: 01740 620253 / 0800 121 4429   FAX: 01740 622 771
www.hardwickhallhotel.co.uk

" The inspiration I gain from working and being involved in Hartlepool comes from its people. The business community is very aware that it is their role to provide job opportunities that enhance and improve people's lives. With the enthusiasm of its people, its historic houses and its great views across the Tees Bay to the Yorkshire Moors beyond, we have a great place to work and live: Hartlepool. "

Martyn Pellew
President NECC
Group Development Director, PD Ports

"When I think of Hartlepool, my fondest memory is of sitting outside Krimo's restaurant on a beautiful warm summer's evening, with the sun setting over the Marina, listening to the quiet flapping of the boat sails in the breeze, the lapping of the water against the boats and their masts knocking together. There is nothing better than good food and great company in a wonderful setting."

Julia Frater
Head of visitTeesvalley

"I cannot think of a better setting for The Tall Ships Races. In particular, I love the view from Hartlepool Marina across to the historic Headland – the past and the present all merging into one. The illuminated HMS Trincomalee at night is also quite breathtaking. One thing that amuses me is the long line of yellow taxis in the town centre; this reminds me of New York."

Andy Saxton
Regional Marketing Manager
GMG Radio (Real Radio)

> " I hope that everyone visiting Hartlepool will have a fantastic experience – and plan to come back again. HMS Trincomalee will still be here – the masts of Hartlepool's very own Tall Ship proudly visible and the cause of many a 'wow' from those seeing her for the first time! In fact, for me, not only the first time, but every time. I look forward to welcoming you on board soon! "

Bryn Hughes
General Manager
HMS Trincomalee Trust

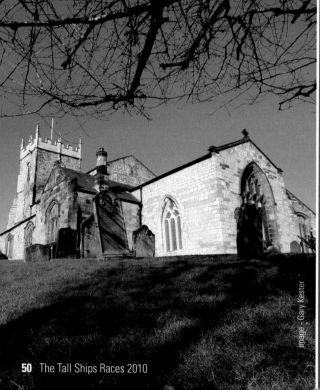

image - Gary Kester

> " As a photographer and filmmaker who specialises in North East subjects and history, I'm very aware of how blessed our town is from a visual perspective. There are few places I can think of that can offer such a variety of dense woodland, rolling fields, long sandy beaches, rocky cliffs and of course some fabulous urban landscapes that combine the very best of ancient and modern architecture – and all within walking distance of each other. "

Gary Kester
Design Manager
Hartlepool College of
Further Education

"I work in the Marina and after work, instead of heading home, I often enjoy a coffee or a beer outside and watch the sun set over the yachts and sink down through the rigging and masts of HMS Trincomalee. Sometimes I head home to get changed and come back again to sample the plethora of culinary delights. I have tried them all, from Japanese sushi to pie and chips, and I'm just as happy in an Irish bar as in a wine bar. Why go abroad when you can enjoy the authentic flavours of so many different countries right here in Hartlepool?"

Allan Henderson
Managing Director, Hartlepool Marina

" Fifteen years ago my colleagues and I bought the Old Customs House, next to the Lock Gates, on Hartlepool Marina. It was to be our Head Office for the next five years. It was a brilliant place to work. There was nothing between us and the North Sea on one side and the Marina on the other. It was mostly undeveloped then, very quiet and a little remote, so it will be fantastic to revisit it in August! "

Geoff Spencer
RDW Creative (formerly Managing Director of Orchid Drinks)

" The year the Tall Ships come to Hartlepool happens to be our 25th year in business, so it's a double celebration for us. Hartlepool has a wonderful Marina which many foreign sailors have praised in a dozen languages, and a multitude of restaurants that bring the world to this haven of ours. It is a friendly and welcoming town that has become my home. Long after the ships have sailed away, I hope you'll come back to rediscover the little hidden gem that is Hartlepool. "

Krimo Bouabda
Managing Director of Krimo's, Portofino and Casa del Mar

“ Hartlepool is extremely vibrant and exciting – there is so much to see and do, from a visit to the Historic Quay to lunch on the Marina. But what makes Hartlepool extra special? It's the people who are proud to live and work here. You are guaranteed a warm welcome and a friendly smile –Hartlepool hospitality will reel you in hook, line and sinker! ”

Joy Yates
Editor, Hartlepool Mail

“ The regenerated marina at Hartlepool will provide a stunning backdrop for the return of the Tall Ships Races to North East England. This prestigious event provides a superb opportunity to showcase Tees Valley and the wider region's assets to thousands of visitors who I know will be given a really warm welcome. I very much look forward to seeing Hartlepool Marina 'in full sail'. I'm sure the atmosphere will be fantastic and everyone will have a wonderful time. ”

Tania Robinson
Head of Marketing
One NorthEast

66 From my point of view, Hartlepool is where imagination and regeneration have come together to create a fantastic visitor experience. The whole town is a hidden gem. With 1,300 years of history on The Headland, a delightful modern Marina with restaurants and bars and the ever enjoyable Hartlepool's Maritime Experience, it all makes for a winning combination. Get there. Be there. Enjoy there. See you there! 99

Jan Williams
North East England Blue Badge Guide

66 Whenever I come back to the town it's the people that make me feel that Hartlepool is somewhere special. They treat me like I've never been away and I know they will give the crews of the ships, and all of the visitors, an equally warm welcome. I think it will be a tremendous event and I'm negotiating with my mother to get my old room back so I can be here too! 99

Jeff Stelling
Sky TV Sports Presenter

"For hundreds of years Hartlepool has been welcoming ships of all sizes — including tall ones. There's something in the heritage of the town that embraces the sea, embraces maritime history, and welcomes people to the town, and it doesn't surprise me in the least that Hartlepool has been able to trade on its past to attract the The Tall Ships Races. I am thrilled the races are here."

Lord Mandelson

"Hartlepool is a dynamic town and the people are very, very friendly. I think everyone will leave with the impression that it's a different place to what they expected and they'll go home feeling they've been given a great welcome by the people of the area."

Sir John Hall

The Volunteer Movement...

" I decided to volunteer with the Tall Ships Races 2010 because it gave me the opportunity to give something back to the town which I grew up in, and which has made me the person I am today. I have also changed a lot in the past few years, and as the races will be a highly visible symbol of Hartlepool's own transformation, I was in no doubt that this was the ideal project to be involved with. "

Gary McTeer
Volunteer, The Tall Ships Races 2010

In broad terms, The Tall Ships Races will see a fleet of between 70–100 ships arrive into the port and will attract an audience of up to one million visitors over four days. An impossibility? A dream? Or just a massive project?

Project managers are fond of asking: How do you eat an elephant? The answer is: You cut it up into bite-sized chunks. This is the approach that has been taken in the delivery of The Tall Ships Races. Every element of the event has been broken down by theme and then allocated to the appropriate responsible partner or stakeholder, and its progress has then been managed and monitored.

But there is a common thread in every strand of the event delivery, without which quality would certainly suffer. That is the input and enthusiasm of the Tall Ships Volunteers.

Over 300 people have offered their time and energy to make the event such a success. From roles involving the berthing and movement of ships to those greeting visitors at the far-flung park-and-ride sites, and everything in between, the volunteers are essential to the smooth running of the event.

Often the unsung heroes, the invisible army, volunteers bring a certain magic to such an event. Motivated by enjoying the experience and making sure that visitors and participants are catered for completely, they each bring a wealth of worldly experience, character and individuality which they are more than keen to let shine and to share. For the visitor this is invaluable – who better to ask where to get that last-minute bottle of water or where to go for the best fish and chips than somebody who is passionate about the event or knowledgeable about and proud of their hometown.

Without the valued support of the volunteers this event wouldn't be half as much fun – many have expressed the desire to progress to volunteering at the London Olympic Games in 2012.

We salute you all!

Welcome to the Tees Valley, and come back soon...

Welcome to the Tees Valley and especially to Hartlepool, this year's venue for The Tall Ships Races.

It is forecast that up to a million visitors will be drawn to Hartlepool's harbour and marina, and the events and attractions surrounding this great occasion promise fascination and fun. There has been growing excitement for many months, not just in Hartlepool but in the wider Tees Valley, and a mounting sense of anticipation, because it gives the Tees Valley a chance to showcase the warmth of its welcome and an opportunity to place the jewel that is Hartlepool in a wider setting.

The Tees Valley is a patchwork of vibrant towns, picturesque villages, gorgeous countryside and exhilarating coastal destinations. Across this colourful landscape there are events and attractions to meet every passion. Explore

fascinating heritage, indulge with shopping, eating out or an overnight stay, or treat the kids to a special trip – not to mention top arts, music, theatre, sports and lots of intriguing experiences to enjoy. It is a place to explore, relax and escape.

Tees Valley enjoys a happy location, nestled between North Yorkshire and County Durham. The five Tees Valley boroughs – Darlington, Hartlepool, Middlesbrough, Redcar & Cleveland and Stockton-on-Tees – all boast a distinctive character, but each shares a commitment to welcoming visitors, and to development and regeneration, as well as pride in our rich tradition of industry and creativity. That pride in our past – including the birthplace of maritime explorer Captain James Cook, the first passenger railway and friction match inventor John Walker – is mirrored by the delight we all share in this place where we live, work and play today. Our surroundings are not as people from afar might

imagine. Yes, we have our petro-chemical industry – an important driver of the UK economy – but the RSPB's magnificent new centre at Saltholme thrives happily cheek-by-jowl with our vital economic activity.

We also have more than 30 miles of spectacular coastline, pretty harbours, busy ports and splendid beach resorts including Seaton Carew and Saltburn-by-the-Sea with its fine pier and magnificent not-to-be-missed water-powered cliff lift. And we enjoy some of the country's most attractive and pleasant green spaces, gently rolling hills and valleys.

In the Tees Valley there's always something new, something different to try out, or a new venue to visit: iconic galleries like mima in Middlesbrough; innovative theatres and many other arts spaces; a diverse programme of festivals including the famed Stockton International Riverside Festival. We have a wealth of attractions and events, hotels and spa facilities – the latest of these being the five-star spa hotel and golf course at Rockliffe Hall near Darlington.

The adrenaline junkies among us can experience white-water rafting at the now Olympic-standard Tees Barrage, as well as race meetings and motor-racing, or even bungee-jumping from the iconic Transporter Bridge. Excellent shopping opportunities abound – just one example is Yarm, nestling in a loop of the River Tees – and you'll find gastronomic delights which demonstrate that we cater for every taste.

We are confident you will be delighted by Hartlepool, its Maritime Experience, and this great chance to greet the Tall Ships. What this means for the Tees Valley is the opportunity to welcome you to the places we call home which will enrich your visitor experience. You will want to come back, and the people of the Tees Valley will welcome you with open arms.

David Kelly,
Chair of visitTeesvalley

Tees Valley, events:

Stockton International Riverside Festival at Stockton-on-Tees Town Centre: 28/07/10- 01/08/10
From the intimate to the truly spectacular, SIRF will again present the very best of street theatre, circus, dance, music and pyrotechnics from around the world in the streets of central Stockton.

Stockton Fringe at Stockton-on-Tees: 29/07/10- 01/08/10
A three-day extravaganza of live music and alternative comedy, Fringe is a real hotbed for new talent, as well as a popular showcase for more experienced performers. This year's event welcomes acts including Calvin Harris, The Human League, The Lightning Seeds and Mercury Rev.

Hartlepool Headland Carnival at Hartlepool Headland: 29/07/10- 10/08/10
The annual carnival is being extended to support the Tall Ships event.

Fighting Ships Exhibition at Hartlepool Art Gallery: 19/6/10 - 28/08/10
Exhibition of the fighting ships during the reign of George III.

Sir Thomas Allen Concert at Tall Ships Village performance stage: 07/08/10 – 07/08/10
Sir Thomas Allen is performing to support the events timetable of the Tall Ships event.

Tall Ships Beacon Event: across each town in Tees Valley 04/08/10
Each town within Tees Valley will come together to light a torch for the launching of The Tall Ships Races.

Billingham International Folklore Festival at various locations across Billingham: 07/08/10 – 14/08/10
A folk music festival, with performances, songs, dance and some music workshops.

Party at the Priory at Gisborough Priory: 07/08/10
An outdoor musical extravaganza featuring the Super Sounds of the 70s and 80s.

Caribbean Carnival Day at Redcar Racecourse: 07/08/10
A great family day out and a chance to dress up in your best pirate costume, Hawaiian shirt or grass skirt, with music from North Tyneside Steelband.

Saltburn Folk Festival at Saltburn Community Hall and Theatre: 13/08/10- 15/08/10
This festival is a non-stop round of ceilidhs, sing-a-arounds, workshops, concerts, folk dance, street entertainment, crafts, markets, competitions and more.

Tees Valley attractions:

Saltholme RSPB, Middlesbrough
A fantastic new wildlife experience in Tees Valley. This beautiful nature reserve is home to a variety of wildlife with a café, visitor centre and children's adventure playground.

Preston Hall Museum and Butterfly World, Yarm, Stockton-on-Tees
Experience exotic butterflies in their natural environment at Butterfly World while Preston Hall Museum offers a fascinating range of exhibitions and is surrounded by beautiful gardens and walkways, perfect for a stroll.

Transporter Bridge and Visitor Centre, Middlesbrough
The only working bridge of its kind in England, this unique structure was originally designed to allow tall ships to pass underneath. It opened in 1911 and can still carry cars and people across the River Tees.

Saltburn-by-the-Sea
This is a traditional Victorian seaside resort with a picturesque beach, pier, cliff lift and many other attractions. Lots to see and do, especially over the Summer.

Middlesbrough Institute of Modern Art (mima), Middlesbrough
mima is a landmark gallery showcasing an internationally significant programme of fine art and applied art from the 1900s to the present day.

Head of Steam, Darlington Railway Museum
Restored 1842 passenger station on the original route of the Stockton and Darlington Railway (the world's first steam-worked public railway). Exhibits relate to railways and include Stephenson's Locomotion of 1825.

Captain Cook Birthplace Museum, Middlesbrough
One of Tees Valley's famous sons, discover why Captain James Cook is the world's most famous navigator with this exploration into his early life, seafaring career and legacy of his voyages.

For more information on all that's going on in Tees Valley go to www.visitteesvalley.co.uk

All aboard for a great event.

As the Exclusive Radio Partner of the Tall Ships' Races, Real Radio is hosting the main stage and broadcasting live from the event. Don't miss it!

real RADIO

100-102fm

The Tall Ships Races 2010

The following pages feature the majestic Tall Ships that will appear at Hartlepool in the summer of 2010.

They are grouped in classes which are outlined beside each Tall Ship together with other details of note. Some will appear in The Tall Ships Races, others only in the North Sea Tall Ships Regatta while some will take part in both.

Collectively they complete the most outstanding array of vessels of all sizes and types to ever gather in Hartlepool's historic waters.

image: tallshipstock.com

A-Z Listings

CLASS A

ALEXANDER VON HUMBOLDT

ASTRID

CHRISTIAN RADICH

DEWARUCI *

EENDRACHT

ISKRA ORP

KALIAKRA *

KAPITAN GLOWACKI *

LOA *

MIR

OOSTERSCHELDE *

PELICAN OF LONDON *

POGORIA

SANTA MARIA MANUELA

SHABAB OMAN

SØRLANDET

STAD AMSTERDAM

STAVROS S NIARCHOS *

TENACIOUS

THOR HEYERDAHL

WYLDE SWAN

CLASS B

AGLAIA

DE GALLANT

JOLIE BRISE *

MAYBE *

MOOSK *

MORNING STAR OF REVELATION

PEGASUS *

PROVIDENT

RUPEL

SWAN *

TECLA

TRINOVANTE

WYVERN

WYVERN AV AALESUND *

CLASS C

BLACK DIAMOND OF DURHAM

BREGO *

CHALLENGER 1 *

CHALLENGER 2 *

DAR SZCZECINA *

DWINGER

FARAMIR *

GAUDEAMUS

JAMES COOK

JOHN LAING

JUAN DE LANGARA *

NEVA

OCEAN SCOUT

OFFSHORE SCOUT

QEENIAN *

RIYAL

SPANIEL

THERMOPYLAE CLIPPER *

WILLIWAW *

ZENOBE GRAMME

ZVEZDA *

CLASS D

DASHER *

ELENA

ENDORFINA *

HANSA *

HEBE III *

LIETUVA

RONA II

RZESZOWIAK *

TOMIDI

URANIA

VITYAZ

ZRYW

* all starred images within the Tall Ships A-Z
supplied by tallshipstock.com

All ships taking part in The Tall Ships Races are correct at
the time of printing, Hartlepool Borough Council cannot
be held responsible for any changes in the names of ships
taking part.

RAMSIDE EVENT CATERING

OFFERS EVENT CATERING BETWEEN YORK AND BERWICK FOR ALL TYPES OF OCCASIONS
WEDDINGS A SPECIALTY

WE CAN COME TO YOUR VENUE OR ALTERNATIVELY WE ARE THE APPROVED CATERERS
FOR TYNEMOUTH PRIORY, SALTWELL PARK, HEXHAM RACECOURSE

"NO JOB TOO SMALL WE'RE JUST HAPPY TO CATER"

OFFICIAL CATERERS FOR THE TALL SHIPS

RAMSIDE EVENT CATERIN
THE LANCASTRIAN SUIT
LANCASTER ROA
DUNSTO
NE11 9J

INFO@RAMSIDEEVENTCATERING.CO.U
TEL. 0191 460535
WWW.RAMSIDEEVENTCATERING.CO.U

RAMSIDE ESTATES LIMITE
RAMSIDE HALL HOTE
TEL. 0191 386 528

ALEXANDER VON HUMBOLDT - The Tall Ships Races

CLASS: A
FLAG: GERMANY
LENGTH: 62.6M
RIG: BARQUE 3
YEAR BUILT: 1906
HOME PORT: BREMEN, GERMANY
ENTERED BY: DEUTSCHE STIFTUNG SAIL TRAINING
LOCATION: WIND ZONE, TALL SHIPS VILLAGE

This ship was launched in 1906 as Sonderburg, but spent most of her life as a lightship called Kiel on Germany's North Sea coast. In 1986, Kiel was bought by the Sail Training Association of Germany (STAG) for reconstruction into a three-masted sailing ship. In 1988, she was renamed Alexander von Humboldt after the famous German naturalist and globetrotter. Shortly after re-launch, she achieved her fastest speed to date of 10.5 knots.

www.dsstalex.de

ASTRID - The Tall Ships Races & North Sea Tall Ships Regatta

This beautiful square-rigged ship offers great sailing with a modern, luxurious interior. However this modernity does not distract from Astrid's spectaculary traditional exterior.

Astrid was built in 1918 as a herring drifter. Until about 1970, she served as a motor ship on the Baltic Sea. During the late seventies the ship was used by the new Lebanese owners for 'dark' jobs during the war in the Near East. There was a suspicion of drug smuggling. A fire the ship suffered off the English coast ended all this. Until 1984 the still elegant hull rusted unused. Then she was rebuilt as a traditional brig, enabling her to cross the Atlantic Ocean as a training ship. The Astrid was extensively rebuilt in 1999 and 2000.

Astrid offers space for up to 50 passengers on day sails and cabins for 24 people on longer voyages. The sanitary fittings are spacious with five toilets and five showers. There is a cosy maritime-furnished lounge with a bar area.

During the longer voyages there is the chance to learn how to sail a square rig sailing vessel. Set sail and climb the rig: you are one of the crew!

On a day sail you will still experience an exciting voyage aboard a traditional sailing vessel. There are many opportunities for corporate hospitality and seminars or daytrips.

www.tallshipastrid.nl

CLASS: A
FLAG: NETHERLANDS
LENGTH: 41.35M
RIG: BRIG
YEAR BUILT: 1918
ENTERED BY: HORIZONSAILING
LOCATION: WIND ZONE, TALL SHIPS VILLAGE

HARTLEPOOL
A MARINA AND MUCH MORE

Nestling on the Tees Valley, Hartlepool is a jewel on the North East Coast and provides a welcome stop for many sailors wanting to experience one of the areas best kept secrets. Hartlepool Marina is one of the most modern marina facilities in Europe, attracting many vessels, the marina is Hartlepool's most alluring and relaxing location, boasting waterside restaurants and romantic promenades. With the expansion of our visitor berths and newly launched On Water activities as well as the abundance of bars, cafes , shops and restaurants of the worlds cuisines there is something to suit everyone day or night, boat owner or water enthusiast.

54° 41' 10" N   1° 12' 45" W

Hartlepools Tall Ship	Walk On Water	Thundercat Racing North East
The 'Adventure'	"It is as close as anyone is going to get to walking on water."	"A power to weight ratio of 340 BHP per tonne puts these inflatable boats firmly in super car territory"
Newly Launched in 2010 to create traditional sailing experiences for all.		
Family /Friends / Colleagues & Corporate	"It is more or less like you are in a hamster ball"	"More fun than a human deserves"

Tel:
(01429) 865 744
Web:
www.hartlepool-marina.com

HARTLEPOOL
A MARINA AND MUCH MORE

INDIVIDUALS / GROUPS / FRIENDS / FAMILIES / COLLEAGUES / CORPORATE

CHRISTIAN RADICH - The Tall Ships Races

CLASS: A
FLAG: NORWAY
LENGTH: 73M
RIG: SHIP
YEAR BUILT: 1937
HOME PORT: OSLO, NORWAY
ENTERED BY: STIFTELSEN SKOLESKIPET CHRISTIAN RADICH
LOCATION: WIND ZONE, TALL SHIPS VILLAGE

Christian Radich functioned as a sail training ship from 1937 to 1998 and still acts as a training ship for the Norwegian Navy during the winter season. During the summer period, the ship offers voyages for school classes, corporate cruises and private parties as well as being a regular participant in The Tall Ships Races, where she has been placed first on corrected time on several occasions.

With almost 9000 metres of rope and a 37.7 metre tall main mast, Christian Radich has proven hard to beat in regattas.
www.radich.no

NHS
Hartlepool

Sign up to MY NHS

My NHS Hartlepool

What is MY NHS?

- It's a way for you to get involved in decisions about local health services

It's free to join and there are lots of other benefits too, including:

- Information to manage your health and well being
- Invitations to consultations, events and surveys
- A subscription to a bi monthly newsletter
- Interactive games and videos

Join MY NHS...

For more information
or to join, visit:
www.hartlepool.nhs.uk
or call freephone
0800 013 0500
and (choose option 5)

DEWARUCI - The Tall Ships Races

*

CLASS: A
FLAG: INDONESIA
LENGTH: 58.3M
RIG: BARQUENTINE 3
YEAR BUILT: 1953
HOME PORT: SURABAYA
ENTERED BY: INDONESIAN NAVY
LOCATION: WIND ZONE, TALL SHIPS VILLAGE

Dewaruci was built in 1952 by H C Stulcken & Sohn Hamburg, West Germany, and launched on 24th January 1953. She sailed to Indonesia with Indonesian naval officers and cadets. The ship has been used as a training ship in the Indonesian Naval Academy based in Surabaya. The mission of KRI Dewaruci is to: provide sea training for Indonesian Naval Cadets; be an Ambassador of goodwill in tourism, culture and information about Indonesia; promote international relationships.

The motto of KRI Dewaruci is "CITA CITA - AKAL BUDI-BERANI JUJUR - GUNA BHAKTI". In English. this means "Morals-Ingenuity-Courage-Loyalty". rucidewa@yahoo.com

EENDRACHT
- The Tall Ships Races & North Sea Tall Ships Regatta

Eendracht is owned and operated by the Dutch Foundation and National Society Het Zeilend Zeeschip.

As a 55m (excluding bowsprit) three-masted schooner, Eendracht replaced her smaller predecessor Johann Smidt and was commissioned by H. M. Queen Beatrix of the Netherlands on 29th August 1989. She is a regular participant in The Tall Ships Races.

www.eendracht.nl

CLASS: A
FLAG: NETHERLANDS
LENGTH: 58.8M
RIG: SCHOONER 3
YEAR BUILT: 1989
HOME PORT: ROTTERDAM
ENTERED BY: STICHTING HET ZEILEND ZEESCHIP
LOCATION: WIND ZONE, TALL SHIPS VILLAGE

ISKRA ORP - The Tall Ships Races

CLASS: A
FLAG: POLAND
LENGTH: 48.36M
RIG: BARQUENTINE 3
YEAR BUILT: 1982
HOME PORT: GYDNIA, POLAND
ENTERED BY: THE POLISH NAVY
LOCATION: WIND ZONE, TALL SHIPS VILLAGE

Iskra Orp is used to train cadets from the Polish Naval Academy during their apprenticeships. The ship was launched on the 6th March 1982 in Gdansk Shipyard.

Iskra Orp is the second sailing ship in Polish Navy to carry this name .The original was a wooden, three-masted gaff schooner Iskra, which sailed under the Polish Navy ensign for 50 years between 1927 and 1977.

www.mw.mil.pl

Middleton Grange
Shopping Centre Hartlepool

www.middleton-grange.co.uk

Image by Duran Photography, www.duranphotography.co.uk

LOCAL STAR · MIDDLETON GRANGE

Local Stars:
Dean & Ryan

Yo ho ho
and a barrel of fun!

During Tall Ships, Middleton Grange will be running a **FREE shuttle bus** to the centre from the Old Cemetery Road, at the entrance to the Headland. PLUS... you will find a number of activities including children's entertainment, photos with the legendary Jack Sparrow and a FREE surf simulator!

We're open 7 days a week and offer over 140 stores, including fashion, jewellery and homeware from Marks & Spencer, River Island, Primark, Argos and New Look.

Visit us at Stand 2E in the Fire Zone.

OVER 140 STORES | FREE SHUTTLE | ONLY 10 MINUTES AWAY | adding value every day

KALIAKRA - North Sea Tall Ships Regatta

CLASS: A
FLAG: BULGARIA
LENGTH: 52.37M
RIG: BARQUENTINE
YEAR BUILT: 1984
HOME PORT: VARNA BULGARIA
ENTERED BY: BULGARIA MARITIME TRAINING CENTRE
LOCATION: WIND ZONE, TALL SHIPS VILLAGE

Kaliakra was built at the Gdansk Shipyard, Poland, in 1984 and is owned by the Bulgarian Maritime Training Centre.

The ship was specially designed for the training and qualification of students from the Maritime Academy in Varna - the future officers of the Bulgarian merchant fleet.

The ship has participated in many Tall Ships Races organised by the International Sailing Training Association (ISTA) and Sail Training International. Her numerous highly placed results and international popularity have raised the prestige of the Bulgarian national flag.

During the Columbus Race 1992 to celebrate the 500 year anniversary of the discovery of America, Kaliakra sailed twice across the Atlantic Sea and finished third overall amongst 143 ships.

www.bmtc-bg.com

KAPITAN GLOWACKI – The Tall Ships Races

*

CLASS: A
FLAG: POLAND
LENGTH: 28.41M
RIG: BRIGANTINE
YEAR BUILT: 1946
HOME PORT: VARNA BULGARIA
ENTERED BY: SAIL TRAINING CENTRE OF POLISH YACHTING ASSOCIATION
LOCATION: MARINA

Kapitan Glowacki was built around 1942 in Germany as a semi-military ship. She was abandoned after the war and found by some Polish people lying in the sand in the North-West corner of Poland. She was quickly renovated as a sailing ship and served as a training vessel undertaking various exercises for maritime schools in Poland during the 1950s, 1960s and part of the 1970s.

In the 1980s she was rebuilt again, this time as a square rigger and used as a school ship for the Polish Sailing Association.

She has been a regular participant in the Tall Ships Races.

www.coz.com.pl

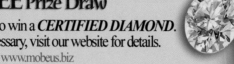

LOA - North Sea Tall Ships Regatta

*

Loa was built as a three-masted schooner in Svendborg, Denmark in 1922 – and restored as a barquentine in Aalborg, Denmark between 2004 and 2008. The vessel is owned by the Danish sail training trust, Tall Ship Aalborg Fonden. The home port is Aalborg, host of the Tall Ships Races in 1999, 2004 and again in 2010. Loa is Denmark's third Class A ship, the two others being the full-rigged ships Danmark and Georg Stage.
www.loa.dk

CLASS: A
FLAG: DENMARK
LENGTH: 38.8M
RIG: BARQUENTINE
YEAR BUILT: 1922
HOME PORT: AALBORG
ENTERED BY: TALL SHIP AALBORG FONDEN
LOCATION: MARINA

MIR - The Tall Ships Races & North Sea Tall Ships Regatta

CLASS: A
FLAG: RUSSIA
LENGTH: 108.8M
RIG: SHIP
YEAR BUILT: 1987
HOME PORT: ST PETERSBURG, RUSSIA
ENTERED BY: ADMIRAL MAKAROV STATE MARITIME ACADEMY, ST. PETERSBURG, RUSSIA
LOCATION: WIND ZONE, TALL SHIPS VILLAGE

Mir, which means Peace, was built as the third of five sister ships at the Lenin, a shipyard in Gdansk, Poland. Based on a new type of design for square-rigged training vessels. Mir's rigging design was slightly altered so that she could sail closer to the wind – up to 30 degrees rather than the usual 60 degrees for square riggers. Mir's full complement of sails is 26. She usually sails with a crew of 200 but can be manned effectively with as few as 30.
www.tall-shipmir.com

OOSTERSCHELDE - North Sea Tall Ships Regatta

*

CLASS: A
FLAG:
NETHERLANDS
LENGTH: 48.62M
RIG: TOPSL SCHOONER
YEAR BUILT: 1918
HOME PORT: ROTTERDAM
ENTERED BY: SHIPPING COMPANY
OOSTERSCHELDE
LOCATION: WIND ZONE,
TALL SHIPS VILLAGE

Oosterschelde was built in the Netherlands in 1918 at the order of the Rotterdam shipping company HAAS and is the last remaining representative of the large fleet of schooners that sailed under the Dutch flag at the beginning of the 20th century. Her name is derived from the eastern part of the Schelde river that flows from France through Belgium and the Netherlands to the sea. Oosterschelde is the largest restored Dutch sailing ship and she acts as a monument for Dutch shipbuilding and maritime navigation under sail.

As a freighter Oosterschelde carried some hundred tons of cargo including bricks, herring and bananas. In 1921, the ship was sold, changing hands three times. She was converted to a motor-sailer before being bought in 1988 and restored to her former glory.

www.oosterschelde.nl

Passionate people. Passionate places.

"The world's largest
offshore wind farm: powered by
North East England."

Steven Parfitt, General Manager, JDR Cable Systems

Hartlepool-based firm JDR Cable Systems is making waves in the provision of subsea power cables, having just been chosen to supply the London Array offshore wind farm – soon to be the largest in the world. With engineering capabilities like these, testing facilities and expertise at Narec (the National Renewable Energy Centre), an established wind power supply chain and sites and infrastructure primed for commercialisation, North East England is leading the way in sustainable energy solutions.

Find out more about North East England's pioneering work in new and renewable energy at
www.northeastengland.co.uk/windpower

PELICAN OF LONDON - The Tall Ships Races & North Sea Tall Ships Regatta

CLASS: A
FLAG: UK
LENGTH: 44.42M
RIG: BARQUENTINE
YEAR BUILT: 1948
HOME PORT: WEYMOUTH
ENTERED BY: PELICAN
PARTNERSHIP L.L.P
LOCATION: WIND ZONE,
TALL SHIPS VILLAGE

Pelican of London is unique among Square Riggers. Her hull form was derived from the elite French clippers of the late 19th century, with a length to breadth ratio of 5:1, a flared bow, fine entry and run. A long poop has been added which provides exceptional space and comfort for worldwide operation.

Her exclusive rig generates twice her engine power and yet it is handy and easily adapted to extreme conditions. She is still family size at 45M (150 ft) LE.

In this total reconstruction only the superb hull of the original 1946 Pelican remains. New bulkheads, new decks, stainless tanks and pipe work, everything is built to the very exacting standards of the latest "Code of Practice for the Safety of Large Commercial Sailing Vessels".

Pelican has been designed principally as a sail training ship, but is capable of many different roles worldwide.
www.adventureundersail.com

BETHESDA GOSPEL HALL, PARK ROAD, HARTLEPOOL, TS26 9HU

For God so loved the world, that He gave His only begotten Son, that whosoever believeth in Him should not perish, but have everlasting life.
John 3 vs 16 - The Bible

Sunday - Gospel Meeting for all at 4.00pm
Tuesday - Adventurers for Children 6pm

www.whatsinit4me.org.uk/bethesdagospelhall.html

POGORIA - The Tall Ships Races & North Sea Tall Ships Regatta

CLASS: A
FLAG: POLAND
LENGTH: 49.52M
RIG: BARQUENTINE
YEAR BUILT: 1980
HOME PORT: GDYNIA, POLAND
ENTERED BY: SAIL TRAINING ASSOCIATION POLAND
LOCATION: WIND ZONE, TALL SHIPS VILLAGE

Pogoria was built in 1980 for the Iron Shackle Fraternity - a marine educational project which was conceived and founded by Captain Adam Jasser in 1971.

The current owner and operator of Pogoria is the Sail Training Association Poland. She is 154 feet long overall with accommodation for up to 50 crew and students.
www.pogoria.pl

GET A WORKOUT WHILE YOU WALK.™

AVAILABLE AT

JULES ⟩

WWW.JULESB.CO.UK

OSBORNE RD, JESMOND, NEWCASTLE UPON TYNE   T: 0191 281 7855   •   STRAMONGATE, KENDAL, CUMBRIA   T: 01539 723 874
HIGH ST, YARM, CLEVELAND   T: 01642 785 342

SANTA MARIA MANUELA - North Sea Tall Ships Regatta

CLASS: A
FLAG: PORTUGAL
LENGTH: 68.64M
RIG: GAFF SCHOONER 4
YEAR BUILT: 1937
ENTERED BY: CAPTAIN. ANTONIO SAO-MARCOS
LOCATION: WIND ZONE, TALL SHIPS VILLAGE

The Santa Maria Manuela, was a four mast Schooner built at the CUF (Companhia União Fabril) in Lisbon in 1937 in a record time of 62 days for the "Empresa de Pesca de Viana".

The high quality steel used, was originaly destined for the construction of two warships which, for a variety of reasons, were never constructed. The steel being then used to construct both the Santa Maria Manuela and her sister ship Creoula.

From that year onwards, acomplished tens of cod fishing expeditions to the banks of Newfoundland and Greenland. On a normal trip she would carry a complement of 54 fishermen, 10 deckhands, 2 cooks, 3 machinists, 2 Navigation Officers and Captain. Could carry more than 12.000 quintais, aproximately 720 metric tons of salted cod and about 60 tons of cod liver oil. Anually, during the winter months, she would be dismasted and all her standing and running gear as well as all her sails would be checked for damages.

She sailed generally under engine and wind power, and thus reach her best speed and manouvre capabilities. She could make good way under bad weather, and could reach 12/13 knots with good weather, covering the route to Portugal in about 9 days. The hull shape of the Santa Maria Manuela is that of the traditional Schooners of the first half of the 20th century used in the cod fishing industry, which became known internationally as the famous "Portuguese White Fleet".

email: santamariamanuela@gmail.com

SHABAB OMAN - The Tall Ships Races & North Sea Tall Ships Regatta

CLASS: A
FLAG: OMAN
LENGTH: 51.46M
RIG: BARQUENTINE
YEAR BUILT: 1971
HOME PORT: OMAN
ENTERED BY: ROYAL NAVY OF OMAN
LOCATION: WIND ZONE, TALL SHIPS VILLAGE

Shabab Oman is now a barquentine, but was launched in 1971 as a topsail schooner called Captain Scott, which operated out of Scotland for the Dulverton Trust. The Trust ran Outward Bound courses for young people lasting 25 days during which time they would be dropped ashore for mountain expeditions and climbing. Captain Scott was laid up in 1975, but bought by the Sultan of Oman in 1977 and renamed Youth of Oman.

In 1979, she was transferred to the Omani Navy and her name converted into Arabic. In 1984, she was converted to a barquentine. Shabab Oman is a regular in The Tall Ships Races and large Tall Ships gatherings around the world, flying the flag for Oman. She is recognised by the red dagger and crossed swords, the national symbol of Oman, on her topsails.
saifalrahbi@yahoo.com

SØRLANDET - The Tall Ships Races

CLASS: A
FLAG: NORWAY
LENGTH: 64.2M
RIG: SHIP
YEAR BUILT: 1927
HOME PORT: KRISTIANSAND, NORWAY
ENTERED BY: STIFTELSEN FULLRIGGEREN SØRLANDET
LOCATION: WIND ZONE, TALL SHIPS VILLAGE

The Sail Training Ship Sørlandet is owned and administrated by a non-profit foundation whose primary objective is to offer the general public the chance to experience life on board a Tall Ship, as well as keeping the ship operational. People of all ages and nationalities are welcomed between 15 and 70 to participate as trainees.

The Sørlandet was built in Kristiansand, Norway, in 1927 as a full-rigged ship intended for training young people for the Merchant Marine. As the demand for regular training of young seamen decreased in the 70s, she extended the activities to welcome the general public on board. The name Sørlandet comes from the southern region of Norway – it means the southern land.
www.schoolship.no

STAD AMSTERDAM - The Tall Ships Races & North Sea Tall Ships Regatta

CLASS: A
FLAG: NETHERLANDS
LENGTH: 74.9M
RIG: SHIP
YEAR BUILT: 2000
HOME PORT: AMSTERDAM, NETHERLANDS
ENTERED BY: CITY OF AMSTERDAM
LOCATION: WIND ZONE, TALL SHIPS VILLAGE

Stad Amsterdam was launched in 2000 as a result of an idea conceived during Sail 1995 and with the combined efforts of the city of Amsterdam and Randstad – a company committed to stimulating employment. The ship was built as a work experience project by unemployed young people and school leavers and now will be used for sail training whilst promoting the city of Amsterdam. www.stadamsterdam.nl

STAVROS S NIARCHOS – The Tall Ships Races & North Sea Tall Ships Regatta

*

CLASS: A
FLAG: UK
LENGTH: 68.05M
RIG: BRIG
YEAR BUILT: 2000
HOME PORT: PORTSMOUTH UK
ENTERED BY: TALL SHIPS YOUTH TRUST
LOCATION: WIND ZONE, TALL SHIPS VILLAGE

STA Stavros S. Niarchos is the first new Tall Ship built in Britain for over 12 years. At 59m it is the maximum size for a brig, the smallest of the square rigs and will accommodate more young people than schooners. The ship is named after the Greek businessman and sailor.

www.tallships.org

TENACIOUS - The Tall Ships Races

CLASS: A
FLAG: UK
LENGTH: 66.56M
RIG: BARQUE 3
YEAR BUILT: 2000
HOME PORT: SOUTHAMPTON
ENTERED BY: JUBILEE SAILING TRUST
LOCATION: WIND ZONE, TALL SHIPS VILLAGE

Tenacious is the largest wooden Tall Ship of her kind in the world. The innovative wood epoxy laminate build started in 1996 with a team made up of skilled designers, engineers, shipwrights and fitters. This team was supported by a volunteer force of over 1500 able bodied and disabled people who came on working shorewatch holidays from all over the UK and abroad.

The ship has access throughout for disabled crew, including wheelchair users, with flat wide decks and powered lifts. There is a speaking compass for the use of blind crew members and bright track radar for partially sighted crew. An induction loop and vibrator alarms have been installed for hard of hearing crew members.

The Jubilee Sailing Trust has been in operation for over 25 years and in that time has taken over 25,000 people to sea including 10,000 people with physical disabilities and 5,000 wheelchair users.

Tenacious competed in The Tall Ships Races for the very first time in 2005 and enjoyed considerable success, finishing second in Class A of the first race from Waterford and fourth in Class A of the NewcastleGateshead to Fredrikstad race.
www.jst.org.uk

THOR HEYERDAHL - The Tall Ships Races & North Sea Tall Ships Regatta

CLASS: A
FLAG: GERMANY
LENGTH: 47.64M
RIG: GAFF SCHOONER
YEAR BUILT: 1930
HOME PORT: KIEL, GERMANY
ENTERED BY: SEGELSCHIFF THOR HEYERDAHL E.V
LOCATION: WIND ZONE, TALL SHIPS VILLAGE

This topsail-schooner has been in service since early 1983. The Thor Heyerdahl is based in the Baltic and the North Sea during the summer months and around the Canary Islands and in the Caribbean during the winter season. Since 1996, the Thor Heyerdahl has been the flagship of High Seas High School (HSHS) which is based in Germany. It sails with students during the winter to South and Middle America in voyages lasting between six and seven months.

This triple-masted topsail-schooner, with an overall length of 50 metres, offers room on board for 32 students and young adults, aiming to bring young people in the age group 15 - 25 years and from all social classes together. All participants are supervised and schooled during their voyage by trained teaching staff and seamen. The Thor Heyerdahl is registered under the number TSG 342 at the STAG (Sail Training Association Germany).

www.th-sailing.de

MAKE THE MOST OF TEES VALLEY ...

There is so much to do in Tees Valley that to help you make the most of your visit we have put together a few suggestions...

DARLINGTON www.visitdarlington.com

Discover shopping with a difference in Darlington, from favourite high street names, unique independent shops, to modern shopping centres and great markets. Add to this the compact, clean, town centre with its pedestrianised heart, modern sculptures, street art, exciting events and a warm Darlington welcome and you have the makings of a great day out. Another Darlington treat is the newly refurbished Head of Steam, telling the story of the history of Darlington and the impact of railways. Many of the highly popular old exhibits still feature, such as the locomotives in the main area of the museum and these are complemented and enhanced with new exhibitions and interactive displays for people of all ages.

MIDDLESBROUGH www.visitmiddlesbrough.com

Middlesbrough contains an exciting mix of old and new. Our rich industrial heritage is proudly represented by the iconic Transporter Bridge and the fearless can bungee jump off this magnificent structure on August 8. At mima until August 15 you will find an exhibition by one of the world's greatest living artists, Anish Kapoor. This coincides with the launch of Temenos, his awe-inspiring sculpture on a grand scale a short distance away. Discover Captain James Cook, the world's most famous navigator, at the Captain Cook Birthplace Museum and enjoy the new exhibition by renowned, locally born artist Mackenzie Thorpe. For great restaurants and award-winning independent fashion boutiques visit Linthorpe Road Central. With so much to see and do, and world-class festivals and events we welcome you on your next visit to the Tees Valley.

REDCAR & CLEVELAND www.visitredcarandcleveland.co.uk

While your in Tees Valley why not take a ride on Britain's oldest remaining water balance cliff lift, opened on the 28th June 1884, Saltburn Cliff Lift links the Spa town of Saltburn to the magnificent pier and promenade. And If you've energy to spare then discover Redcar & Cleveland's great outdoors and try out many of the activities available to you, whether it be cycling, walking, birdwatching, surfing, fishing, rally driving, go karting, quad biking, golf, horse racing...exhilarated yet? You will be!

Our magnificent coastline is the perfect haven for watersport enthusiasts, surfers flock from all over the country to sample the waves at Saltburn and the increasingly popular kite surfing at Redcar.

STOCKTON www.visitstockton.co.uk

Walking along the Tees, at the heart of Stockton, you will see breathtaking views, amazing architecture in the form of the award-winning Infinity Bridge and the world-class Tees Barrage, a haven for nature, flora and fauna and fantastic facilities for sportsmen and women of all abilities. Stockton's annual Take to the Tees festival gives everyone the chance to come and have a go at a wide range of watersports, and is just one of a number of exciting signature festivals which bring a feel-good, carnival spirit to the borough. Take a trip along to the Tees aboard the Teesside Princess and head to Yarm, which was voted 'Best High Street' in Britain in a BBC poll. Yarm is a pretty, cosmopolitan town filled with independent boutique shops, pubs and restaurants. One visit and you can guarantee you will return to sample the town's charm and hospitality.

WYLDE SWAN - The Tall Ships Races & North Sea Tall Ships Regatta

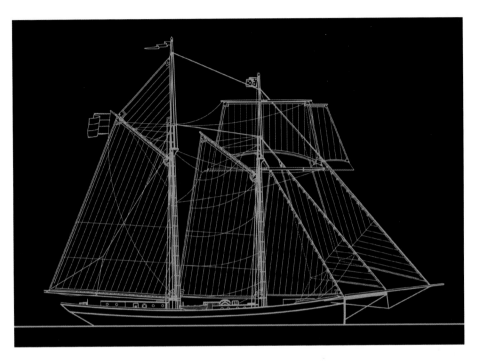

CLASS: A
FLAG: NETHERLANDS
LENGTH: 62M
RIG: SCHOONER 2
YEAR BUILT: 2010
HOME PORT: MAKKUM, NETHERLANDS
ENTERED BY: SWAN FAN MAKKUM
LOCATION: WIND ZONE, TALL SHIPS VILLAGE

Built on the hull of a traditional herring hunter, Wylde Swan combines spectacular sailing characteristics with spacious indoor facilities that can comfortably accommodate large groups.

Wylde Swan is the latest addition to the international fleet of tall ships.
With a length over all of 62 meters and 1130 M2 sail area, Wylde Swan is an exciting two mast topsail schooner.

The highly succesful and reliable company "Swan fan Makkum Charters", well known for its expertise in tallship sailing, sail training and chartering, started this ambitious project in 2008 and will proudly present Wylde Swan at Sail 2010
www.wyldeswan.com

AGLAIA - The Tall Ships Races & North Sea Tall Ships Regatta

CLASS: B
FLAG: AUSTRIA
LENGTH: 15.36M
RIG: GAFF KETCH
YEAR BUILT: 1998
HOME PORT: VIENNA, AUSTRIA
ENTERED BY: HEIKO UHLENBERG SAITRAINING
LOCATION: MARINA

Aglaia was built by the Colin Archer Club in Stockholm, a club that was founded in 1975 to rebuild hulls based on the famous Norwegian rescue vessels of the last century. Her hull was one of 30 built at the time and bought by a salesman from Hamburg in Germany, who worked on completing the ship himself. However, after 15 years of work, he died in the early 1990s. His sons took four years to sell the unfinished vessel, but in 1996, she was bought by the non-profit organisation Segeln ohne Grenzen e.V., which means Sailing without Borders. In June 1997 Aglaia was completed and ready for her maiden voyage.
www.sail-aglaia.com

DE GALLANT - The Tall Ships Races & North Sea Tall Ships Regatta

CLASS: B
FLAG: NETHERLANDS
LENGTH: 36.05M
RIG: GAFF SCHOONER 2
YEAR BUILT: 1916
HOME PORT: AMSTERDAM
ENTERED BY: STICHTING ZEILSCHIP DE GALLANT
LOCATION: WIND ZONE, TALL SHIPS VILLAGE

De Gallant was launched in 1916 under the name Jannetje Margaretha in Vlaardingen. She served as a herring lugger in the North Sea until 1936. In 1982 she was used as a cargo vessel by her Danish owner. Then in 1987 she returned to the Netherlands and was fully restored by a teaching and work experience project for youth in Amsterdam.
www.degallant.nl

JOLIE BRISE - The Tall Ships Races & North Sea Tall Ships Regatta

CLASS: B
FLAG: UK
LENGTH: 22.4M
RIG: GAFF CUTTER
YEAR BUILT: 1913
HOME PORT: HAMBLE, ENGLAND
ENTERED BY: DAUNTSEY'S SCHOOL, WILTSHIRE, ENGLAND
LOCATION: MARINA

Jolie Brise is a 56' gaff rigged pilot cutter that was built in La Havre in 1913. In 1925, she was the inaugural winner of the Fastnet Race, repeating the success in 1929 and 1930 and is still the only vessel to have won the Fastnet three times. Her most noted achievement was her rescue of all but one of the crew of the schooner, Adriana, which caught fire during the 1932 Bermuda Race.

She is now owned by Dauntsey's School Sailing Club. The school started a sailing club in the 1970s when some pupils placed an advert in the Times saying:"slave gang from Wiltshire offers free labour to owner of embarrassingly large yacht in return for some free sailing". They gained the use of Griffin II which was rebuilt by the school, but was tragically wrecked when she broke free of her moorings in Portland Harbour.
www.joliebrise.comq

CLASS: B
FLAG: UK
LENGTH: 26.13M
RIG: BM KETCH
YEAR BUILT: 1929
ENTERED BY: STEVE SWALLOW
LOCATION: MARINA

MAYBE
- The Tall Ships Races & North Sea Tall Ships Regatta

Maybe, launched in 1933, was designed for round the world cruising and built by De Vries Lentsch, Amsterdam for Jan Jacob van Rietschoten. She was hidden during the Second World War and afterwards she underwent a complete refit with a new rig. Maybe took part in the first Tall Ships Races in 1956.

She sailed mainly around the Mediterranean and in the 70s regularly crossed the Atlantic between the West Indies and the Mediterranean. In the 80s she also sailed through the Panama Canal and up the east coast of the USA to Canada. She was sold to the present owners in 1989 and underwent another complete restoration, returning to sailing in 2007 around Scotland and then onto Spain last year.
maybe.sailing@gmail.com

PROUD SPONSORS OF THE HARTLEPOOL TALL SHIPS RACES 2010

TEESPORT CONTAINER TERMINAL 2

2·2

THE TALL SHIPS RACES 2010

Hartlepool

Presented by Szczecin

Sail Training International

PD Ports is a specialist ports business delivering solutions to improve supply chains.

With operations at Teesport and throughout Humberside, PD Ports provides a comprehensive range of port and shipping services, catering for the full port and logistics needs of its customers.

From cargo handling to transport, stevedoring to warehousing, PD Ports is the logical link.

For further information, contact Kirsten Potter on +44 (0)1642 877026 or email kirsten.potter@pdports.co.uk www.pdports.co.uk

PD PORTS

A Brookfield Ports Company

MOOSK - The Tall Ships Races

CLASS: B
FLAG: UK
LENGTH: 17.3M
RIG: GAFF YAWL
YEAR BUILT: 1906
HOME PORT: PLYMOUTH, UK
ENTERED BY: CREMYLL SAILING
LOCATION: MARINA

*

Moosk is a recent entry in The Tall Ships fleet; however, she is one of the oldest. She was built as a gentleman's yacht in Falmouth in 1906 to Lloyds' A1 specifications. After a full life with many different owners, she was abandoned during the 1970s in the outskirts of Glasgow. Cremyll Sailing found her hull there in 1999 and started off with the project of rebuilding her completely for sail training with young people for a maximum of eight trainees on board. The hull was in excellent condition, considering the lack of care it experienced. However the rebuild was quite extensive and she was eventually ready to sail in 2001. Since then her voyages have gradually expanded, until last year, when she took part in the famous 50th Anniversary Tall Ships Races across to Spain. www.cremyll-sailing.org.uk

MORNING STAR OF REVELATION
- The Tall Ships Races

CLASS: B
FLAG: UK
LENGTH: 18.9M
RIG: GAFF KETCH
YEAR BUILT: 1978
HOME PORT: CHATHAM, KENT, UK
ENTERED BY: MORNING STAR TRUST
LOCATION: MARINA

The Morning Star Trust has been taking people safely to sea under sail for over 25 years. The Trust operates two yachts, Morning Star of Revelation (a 62ft gaff ketch) and the training yacht Dayspring (a 36ft Bermudan sloop) and specialises in activities to suit the Duke of Edinburgh's Gold Award residential section. Cruising areas include the Thames Estuary, South Coast of England, Belgium, France and Holland. www.morningstar.org.uk

PEGASUS - The Tall Ships Races

CLASS: B
FLAG: UK
LENGTH: 22.09M
RIG: GAFF CUTTER
YEAR BUILT: 2008
HOME PORT: EXETER
ENTERED BY: ISLAND CUTTER LTD
LOCATION: MARINA

*

Pegasus is a newly built Pilot Cutter, a type known for speed and seaworthiness. She is exciting to sail, comfortable and safe. She is ideal for the sail training role she was built for, having been constructed as a hands-on vessel. Island Cutter know how to get the best out of the boat and the best from the people onboard. Pegasus is also available for private charter, solo travellers, couples, beginners or experts at the helm all are welcome to join and sail Pegasus. A trip aboard Pegasus offers fantastic food, wonderful like-minded company, and the very best in traditional sailing. www.islandcutter.co.uk

PROVIDENT - The Tall Ships Races

CLASS: B
FLAG: UK
LENGTH: 27.1M
RIG: GAFF KETCH
YEAR BUILT: 1924
HOME PORT: BRIXHAM
ENTERED BY: TRINITY SAILING FOUNDATION
LOCATION: MARINA

Provident is owned and run by Trinity Sailing Foundation, which also runs two other traditional Brixham sailing vessels – Leader and Golden Vanity. All three were built on the Dart river at Galmpton. Leader and Provident are two of the last working sailing trawlers still afloat.

Provident is 95 feet long and weighs 85 tonnes. She was built in 1924, as a replacement for an earlier vessel of the same name, sunk during the First World War. After a period in private ownership, she arrived in Salcombe in 1951, where she became the founding vessel of the Island Cruising Club.

In the late 1980s, Provident underwent a major refit, and was re-launched in 1991. She continued to sail with the ICC until 1999, when she started working from Brixham as part of the Trinity Sailing Foundation. www.trinitysailing.co.uk

RUPEL

- The Tall Ships Races & North Sea Tall Ships Regatta

CLASS: B
FLAG: BELGIUM
LENGTH: 19.85M
RIG: GAFF SCHOONER 2
YEAR BUILT: 1996
HOME PORT: BOOM, BELGIUM
ENTERED BY: JAN VANDENBORNE
LOCATION: MARINA

Rupel was built on the banks of the river Rupel by unemployed youngsters and launched in 1996. The project provided these young people with skills that would help them find jobs more easily.

In the summer, Rupel sails the Belgian coastline and takes part in The Tall Ships Races and other events in Northern Europe. www.rupel.be

SWAN - The Tall Ships Races

CLASS: B
FLAG: UK
LENGTH: 26.12M
RIG: GAFF KETCH
YEAR BUILT: 1900
HOME PORT: LERWICK, SCOTLAND
ENTERED BY: THE SWAN TRUST
LOCATION: MARINA

Swan was built in May 1900 and is a Fifie, which was a vessel unique to the Scottish Herring Fleet. She fished for herring, becoming the last of five herring sailing boats left in Shetland, until 1935 when an engine was fitted.

After the Second World War, Swan continued fishing with the seine net until the 1950s when she was retired and taken south as a houseboat. In 1990 she was acquired by the newly formed Swan Trust, which restored her to a Shetland Smack – a gaff-rigged ketch. Their purpose was to restore and re-rig Swan as a seagoing sail-fishing boat using authentic materials and preserving Shetland's maritime heritage.

The Trust also aims to encourage young people to sail on her keeping alive traditional techniques of sailing and fishing in the area. www.swantrust.com

TECLA - The Tall Ships Races & North Sea Tall Ships Regatta

CLASS: B
FLAG: NETHERLANDS
LENGTH: 39.5M
RIG: GAFF KETCH 2
YEAR BUILT: 1915
HOME PORT: WINKEL
ENTERED BY: JAN BOUWMAN & JANNETTE SLUIK
LOCATION: MARINA

Tecla was built in Vlaardingen, in the south of Holland, originally as a fishing boat for herrings. Launched under the name of Graaf van Limburg Stirum she fished the Dogger Bank for over ten years. As the fishing fleet shrunk she was sold to Denmark to become a freighter under the name of Tecla. She returned to Holland in the 1980s to be re-fitted as a sail training vessel.

She is now owned by a family of four and she is one of the most original and beautiful sail training vessels in Europe. On board trainees from all over the world learn how to sail a vessel with a gaff rig and learn how to navigate near land and on open waters. Tecla has competed in The Tall Ships Races 2008 and Funchal 500 Tall Ships Races in which she came first in her Class from Ilhavo, Portugal to Funchal, Madeira.
www.tecla.nl

CLASS: B
FLAG: UK
LENGTH: 24.7M
RIG: GAFF SCHOONER
YEAR BUILT: 1994
ENTERED BY: SCHOONERSAIL
LOCATION: MARINA

TRINOVANTE
- The Tall Ships Races & North Sea Tall Ships Regatta

The schooner Trinovante is run by Schoonersail and anyone over 18 can apply to sail onboard. The ship's emphasis is on exploring European waters under sail and encouraging good seamanship skills in a relaxed, friendly atmosphere.

Trinovante takes a maximum of eight trainees at any one time and has a permanent skipper and mate who have been sailing her for the last five years. Every year sees Trinovante running a number of taster weekends in the UK before setting off on her summer voyage. In the last few years Trinovante has sailed round Britain twice.

All the details of this year's voyage and also a short film are on the website. www.schoonersail.com

Affordable

Wynyard Hall
Country House Hotel

Luxury

Wynyard Hall, Tees Valley TS22 5NF
Tel: 01740 644811
www.wynyardhall.co.uk

WYVERN
- The Tall Ships Races

CLASS: B
FLAG: NORWAY
LENGTH: 24.25M
RIG: GAFF KETCH
YEAR BUILT: 1897
HOME PORT: STAVANGER
ENTERED BY: STAVANGER MARITIME MUSEUM
LOCATION: MARINA

In 1894, the world famous ship designer Colin Archer of Larvik received a very special commission for the English timber merchant Frederick Croft who ordered a high-class yacht.
The vessel was launched on 10 August 1897, and named Wyvern from mythology which means 'an awe-inspiring dragon'. Frederick Croft was an enthusiastic sailor and crossed the North Sea many times, visiting among other places, Hull, the place where he was born. In 1909, Wyvern was sold to Kiel and renamed Tatjana, sailing under the German flag until after World War I, when she returned to Norway.
In 1924, she was bought by a well-known newspaper editor who kept her for 10 years until 1934 when she was sold to a British couple Anne and Terrence Carr. They lived onboard and sailed for 27 years until 1973, crossing the Atlantic 12 times, and sailed around the world during the 1950s.
www.stavanger.museum.no

WYVERN AV AALESUND - The Tall Ships Races

CLASS: B
FLAG: NORWAY
LENGTH: 24.25M
RIG: GAFF KETCH
YEAR BUILT: 1995
HOME PORT: AALESUND
ENTERED BY: WYVERN II A/S
LOCATION: MARINA

*

Wyvern av Aalesund was built in Abeking and Rasmussen between 1993 and 1995. She is a true copy of the legendary Wyvern (Colin Archer design) built in 1897, Norway.

She was built to be a schoolship and became part of the DJS Clipper fleet in Hamburg. Wyvern II A/S bought Wyvern av Aalesund in May 2009 and she became Alesund's official training ship.
www.wyvernavaalesund.no

BLACK DIAMOND OF DURHAM -
The Tall Ships Races & North Sea Tall Ships Regatta

CLASS: C
FLAG: UK
LENGTH: 13.5M
RIG: BM SLOOP
YEAR BUILT: 1972
HOME PORT: HARTLEPOOL, UK
ENTERED BY: SAILING NORTH EAST
LOCATION: MARINA

Black Diamond of Durham was commissioned in 1972 for her original owner, Lt Cdr Lewis RN, who fitted her out to his own specification and raced her on the South coast.

In the early 1990s, Black Diamond was purchased by the Farimar Trust who stripped and refitted her for sail training. She was used in the North East of England for sail training, offering a sailing experience to young people from a disadvantaged background. Black Diamond has not missed a Tall Ships Races since then. Purchased by Sailing North East in 1999, she has been refitted again for a different type of client – corporate entertainment and teambuilding along with conventional sail training. www.sailingnortheast.co.uk

BREGO - The Tall Ships Races

CLASS: C
FLAG: POLAND
LENGTH: 13.3M
RIG: BM KETCH
YEAR BUILT: 1988
HOME PORT: WROCLAW
ENTERED BY: HOBBIT FOUNDATION
LOCATION: MARINA

The Hobbit Foundation is a non-gov organisation for free time activities of youth and children. For over 12 years they have organised multiple sea-culture workshops, shanty music concerts, sailing and training camps and sea cruises. Their aim is to educate by sailing, that is to create opportunities for self-development and getting to know new places and people. In Spring 2004 they took possession of s/y Brego, former s/y Tato. This is a 10 ton Bermudan ketch. The name of the yacht comes from Tolkien's Triology. They are seeking contacts with organisations like theirs from different nations. www.fundacja-hobbit.pl/zagle

CLASS: C
FLAG: UK
LENGTH: 22M
RIG: BM CUTTER
YEAR BUILT: 2000
HOME PORT: PORTSMOUTH
ENTERED BY: TALL SHIPS YOUTH TRUST
LOCATION: MARINA

CHALLENGER 1 AND CHALLENGER 2
- The Tall Ships Races

Tall Ships Challenger 1

Tall Ships Challenger 2

The Tall Ships Challenger Fleet yachts are 22 metre (72 foot) steel hulls built in 2000 and designed to race around the world "the wrong way" (against prevailing wind and tide), so are exceptionally strong and seaworthy.

There are four yachts in the Challenger fleet and they are operated by the Tall Ships Youth Trust. The charity, which celebrated its 50th anniversary in 2007, also operates the brig Stavros S Niarchos.

The Challengers, which can each accommodate a crew of up to 18, previously took part in the Round the World Challenge races. They are modern, safe, purpose-built yachts, perfect for sail training and coastal adventures. With a Bermudan Cutter Rig, the Challengers can sail with a mainsail, two headsails and a spinnaker. They have a large cockpit, sturdy decks and a state of the art navigational suite.
www.tallships.org

DAR SZCZECINA - The Tall Ships Races & North Sea Tall Ships Regatta

CLASS: C
FLAG: POLAND
LENGTH: 18.15M
RIG: BM SLOOP
YEAR BUILT: 1969
HOME PORT: SZCZECIN
ENTERED BY: GMINA MIASTO SZCZECIN
LOCATION: MARINA

Dar Szczecina is owned by the City of Szczecin in Poland and has undertaken many of The Tall Ships Races since 1976, normally manned by students from the city. The vessel's name means 'gift of Szczecin'.
www.dar.szczecina.wp.pl

DWINGER
- North Sea Tall Ships Regatta

CLASS: C
FLAG: NETHERLANDS
LENGTH: 48.5M
RIG: BM SLOOP
YEAR BUILT: 2009
HOME PORT: ZAANDAM, NETHERLANDS
ENTERED BY: N. P.J SANDMANN
LOCATION: MARINA

Originally the ship was designed by Ted Hood as a Ketch rigged sailing vessel for the Royal Huisman shipyard in the Netherlands.

The Royal Huisman shipyard built the hull and sold it to the present owner in 2001. Mr Sandmann, the owner, wanted something special for his ship so together with Gerard Dijkstra Naval Architects he redesigned it into an Aerorigg sloop. In 2001, construction started in Zaandam at the owner's private yard. The 62 meter spar of the aerorigg was built on the same yard and finished in November 2005. npjsandmann@hotmail.com

....

CLASS: C
FLAG: UK
LENGTH: 22M
RIG: BM KETCH
YEAR BUILT: 1982
ENTERED BY: THE CIRDAN SAILING TRUST
LOCATION: MARINA

FARAMIR
- The Tall Ships Races

*

Faramir, a ketch with a length of 22.35m and a breadth of 5.26m, was designed by Marine Architect David Cannell in 1982, specifically for use as a sail training vessel for an organisation called Shaftsbury Homes & Arethusa, from where she gained her original name, Arethusa.

In 2002, after many years of service, during which she developed a following of loyal sailors, Arethusa was sold on to another sail training organisation who changed her name to Bulldog. Not being able to fulfil her potential, her owners sold her to The Cirdan Sailing Trust in January 2006.

Being absolutely ideal for the work undertaken by The Cirdan Sailing Trust, she was purchased to replace the vessel Hartlepool Renaissance which had to be retired from service at the end of the 2005 season. It was necessary to change her name again, and the vessel was renamed Faramir after Cirdan's sister charity with which it joined forces in 2002. www.cirdansailing.com

Get into money saving offers.

See what's going on in Newcastle and save money doing it.

visit: **getintonewcastle.co.uk**

GAUDEAMUS
- The Tall Ships Races
& North Sea Tall Ships Regatta

CLASS: C
FLAG: POLAND
LENGTH: 13.35M
RIG: BM SLOOP
YEAR BUILT: 1986
ENTERED BY: JK AZS SZCZECIN
LOCATION: MARINA

Gaudeamus is a beautiful and fast boat for racing pedigree, built in the Naval Shipyard. L. Teligi w Szczecinie. She participated in several voyages to the Baltic and North Seas. Gaudeamus took part in The Tall Ships Races 2007 and 2008 where the second race from Bergen to Den Helder took 3rd place in his class, he was also in New York.

JAMES COOK - The Tall Ships Races

The James Cook is named after Captain James Cook, RN, FRS, probably one of the greatest sailors, explorers and navigators ever to go to sea, and she spends much of her time sailing the North Sea waters where the young Cook learned his sailing skills.

CLASS: C
FLAG: UK
LENGTH: 20.95M
RIG: BM KETCH
YEAR BUILT: 1986
HOME PORT: NEWCASTLE, UK
ENTERED BY: OCEAN YOUTH TRUST NORTH EAST LTD
LOCATION: MARINA

A tough 22 metre steel ketch, James Cook has the accolade of circumnavigating the globe under sail. In addition to her annual appearance in The Tall Ships' Races, James Cook provides sailing opportunities for young people that include weekend taster trips, week-long RYA Competent Crew qualifying passages and cross-North Sea trips to the Baltic Sea and the Netherlands.
www.sailjamescook.com

FINE INDIVIDUAL FURNITURE

JL DESIGN DESIGN IN KITCHENS & INTERIORS

4b Poplar Court, Atley Way, Nelson Park Industrial Estate,
Cramlington, Northumberland. NE23 1WR
Tel: 01670 712271 www.jldesignkitchens.co.uk

JOHN LAING - The Tall Ships Races

CLASS: C
FLAG: UK
LENGTH: 20.95M
RIG: BM KETCH
YEAR BUILT: 1987
HOME PORT: GOSPORT
ENTERED BY: OCEAN YOUTH TRUST SOUTH
LOCATION: MARINA

John Laing is a Shipwright Class steel Bermudan ketch that was built for the Ocean Youth Club in 1990. She is now operated by Ocean Youth Trust South from her home base in Southampton and takes many hundreds of young people on sail training voyages from March to November each year. www.oytsouth.org

JUAN DE LANGARA
- North Sea Tall Ships Regatta

CLASS: C
FLAG: SPAIN
LENGTH: 18.3M
RIG: BM SCHOONER 2
YEAR BUILT: 1983
HOME PORT: LA CORUNA, SPAIN
ENTERED BY: ASOCIACION JUAN DE LANGARA
LOCATION: MARINA

After the Cutty Sark Tall Ships' Races in 1990, a group of liaison officers from La Coruna, who were all sailors, were so taken with the philosophy of the races and the sail training experience they decided to charter a boat and race themselves. This group ran the Liaison Office when the Cutty Sark Tall Ships' Races returned to La Coruna in 1994 then chartered Ice Maiden for the races in 1996, receiving sponsorship from the La Coruna port authority.

Motivated by the ideals of sail training and inspired by Robin Duchesne to start a sail training organisation, they chartered vessels again in 1997 and 1998, but in 1999 decided to buy their own boat so that they could regularly race in The Tall Ships Races. Although very young, they each contributed as much as they could and, receiving sponsorship once again from the town of La Coruna, they bought Juan de Langara. www.langara.org/?lang=en

*

NEVA - The Tall Ships Races

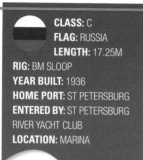

CLASS: C
FLAG: RUSSIA
LENGTH: 17.25M
RIG: BM SLOOP
YEAR BUILT: 1936
HOME PORT: ST PETERSBURG
ENTERED BY: ST PETERSBURG RIVER YACHT CLUB
LOCATION: MARINA

Neva was first launched in 1936 at the Abeking & Rasmussen yard in the German city of Bremen. She was originally named Ibis, after a type of bird. She was one of nine boats built to the same design and named after different birds – the boats were nicknamed the 'bird' series.

Since 1975, Neva again became part of the sailing fleet of the city of Leningrad and began to actively participate in sailing competitions. Through the efforts of her crew and a supply of new young trainees, she regularly won prizes. From 1991, Neva began to take part in international regattas, and even be among the winners. Every year since 1995, Neva has made long-distance sea-training trips to the Baltic Sea with the purpose of passing on the invaluable experience of maritime veterans to young sailors.

OCEAN SCOUT - The Tall Ships Races
& North Sea Tall Ships Regatta

Sister ships Ocean Scout and Offshore Scout are 15 metre Oyster 49 deck saloon ketches. They operate from the East Coast port of Ipswich, sailing weekend and longer cruises with crews of up to 11 young people drawn from schools, youth groups and Scouting organisations.

CLASS: C
FLAG: UK
LENGTH: 14.94M
RIG: BM KETCH
YEAR BUILT: 1993
HOME PORT: WEST MERSEA, ESSEX, UK
ENTERED BY: ADVENTURES OFFSHORE
LOCATION: MARINA

Adventures Offshore has its roots in the Scouting movement and has been offering sail training since 1964. It is a charitable trust based on the picturesque Island of Mersea, nestled between the Essex rivers Blackwater and Colne.
www.adventuresoffshore.co.uk

CLASS: C
FLAG: UK
LENGTH: 14.94M
RIG: BM KETCH
YEAR BUILT: 1997
HOME PORT: WEST MERSEA, ESSEX, UK
ENTERED BY: ADVENTURES OFFSHORE
LOCATION: MARINA

OFFSHORE SCOUT - The Tall Ships Races

Sister ships Offshore and Ocean Scout are 15 metre Oyster 49 deck saloon ketches. They operate from the East Coast port of Ipswich, sailing weekend and longer cruises with crews of up to 11 young people drawn from Schools, Youth Groups and Scouting organisations.

Adventures Offshore has its roots in the Scouting movement and has been offering sail training since 1964. It is a charitable trust based on the picturesque Island of Mersea, nestled between the Essex rivers Blackwater and Colne.
www.adventuresoffshore.co.uk

QEENIAN
- The Tall Ships Races

Qeenian is a Bermudan sloop, completed in 2008: a combination of classical design and modern technology. Her home port is Gdansk, Poland.
www.qeenian.pl

CLASS: C
FLAG: POLAND
LENGTH: 20.57M
RIG: BM SLOOP
YEAR BUILT: 2007
HOME PORT: GDANSK
ENTERED BY: ROCKFIELD JURATA SP.Z.O.O.
LOCATION: MARINA

Where are you spending the night?

You decide.

Drink to enjoy, not to regret.

Safer Hartlepool · CLEVELAND POLICE

Safer Hartlepool

The Safer Hartlepool Partnership works alongside partners to make Hartlepool a safer place for all its communities whether a resident or visitor to the town.

To ensure that you make the most of your stay, we would like to give out some important reminders on how to enjoy a safe visit.

Always remember to keep your personal belongings on you at all times.

Keep wallets, purses, credit and debit cards out of sight.

If you accompanying children remember to keep them in full view at all times.

Always ensure all doors and windows are secure before leaving your vehicle.

Don't leave anything on display and take all your possessions with you when you leave your vehicle.

We hope you have a safe and enjoyable stay.

Visit www.saferhartlepool.co.uk for more information about the Partnership

RIYAL - North Sea Tall Ships Regatta

CLASS: C
FLAG: NETHERLANDS
LENGTH: 10.93M
RIG: BM SLOOP
YEAR BUILT: 1983
ENTERED BY: RJ ALBRINK
LOCATION: MARINA

This boat was built by Rival Bowman Yachts for a Canadian couple, to allow them to sail the world in comfort. The boat was shown at the Earls Court Boat Show in 1983 and as one of the finest examples ever built, it's been on the cover of the R36 brochures of the Rival Bowman shipyard for many years.

After a circumnavigation and many years in remote locations around the world, followed by an extensive refit in the recent years this boat was bought by the current owner in the spring of 2009.
bertalbrink@gmail.com

SPANIEL - The Tall Ships Races & North Sea Tall Ships Regatta

CLASS: C
FLAG: LATVIA
LENGTH: 17.06M
RIG: BM SLOOP
YEAR BUILT: 1979
HOME PORT: RIGA, LATVIA
ENTERED BY: GUNARS STEINERTS
LOCATION: MARINA

Spaniel was designed and built in Poland in 1979 as a single-handed ocean racer. In 1980, Polish yachtsmen took line honours in the Ostar 80 race after a 19 day Westward Atlantic Crossing. From 1982-97 Spaniel was used by the Academy of Science for research purposes and occasional cruising and racing.
Privately owned since 1997, Spaniel is used for sail training Latvian youngsters. The vessel has also enjoyed successes in many of The Tall Ships Races.
www.spaniel.lv

THERMOPYLAE CLIPPER
- The Tall Ships Races & North Sea Tall Ships Regatta

CLASS: C
FLAG: UK
LENGTH: 18.3M
RIG: BM CUTTER
YEAR BUILT: 1996
HOME PORT: SOUTHAMPTON, UK
ENTERED BY: DISCOVERY SAILING PROJECT
LOCATION: MARINA

*

Thermopylae Clipper is the latest addition to the Discovery Sailing Project fleet and is based on the River Hamble near Southampton. This legendary yacht is a 60 foot cutter built by Colvic Craft in the UK in 1996 and has a great history. She was designed for the Clipper Round the World race and has been raced around the world four times previously, being renamed Leeds and later Hong Kong for those voyages. Now, she retains her original name Thermopylae Clipper.

The vessel is very sturdy and spacious. Accommodation is simple and utilitarian, but seamanlike. There are individual bunks with good storage for kit, large galley and spacious communal spaces, two heads (toilets) and one shower. The vessel is fitted out to accommodate 15 people. www.dsp.uk.com

WILLIWAW
- The Tall Ships Races & North Sea Tall Ships Regatta

CLASS: C
FLAG: BELGIUM
LENGTH: 14.45M
RIG: BM KETCH
YEAR BUILT: 1970
HOME PORT: ANTWERP
ENTERED BY: SAIL TRAINING ASSOCIATION BELGIUM
LOCATION: MARINA

*

Williwaw belongs to the Sail Training Association of Belgium (S.T.A.B.), having been entrusted to them from the city of Antwerp in 1998. S.T.A.B. completed a total restoration of Williwaw using volunteers and help from the National Maritime Museum. Onboard Williwaw, a world traveller named Willy de Roos first circumnavigated the American continent from east to west, sailing via the northwest passage in Greenland and the Bering Strait, reaching the west coast of North America before sailing onto Antartica in 1979.

Williwaw is used for sail training young people and is a floating ambassador for the National Maritime Museum in Antwerp. In winter she is moored at the museum dock and in summer sails with young people onboard. She is a regular participant in The Tall Ships Races. www.sailtraining.be

ZENOBE GRAMME - The Tall Ships Races

CLASS: C
FLAG: BELGIUM
LENGTH: 28.15M
RIG: BM KETCH
YEAR BUILT: 1961
HOME PORT: ZEEBRUGGE, BELGIUM
ENTERED BY: BELGIAN NAVY
LOCATION: MARINA

The Sail Training Ship Zénobe Gramme was originally designed as an oceanographic research vessel by the naval architect Van Dijck and was built in 1961 at the former Boel shipyards in Temse, Belgium. She is named after the scientist Zénobe Gramme, the inventor of the dynamo (1869). She was used as a research vessel until 1970, and since then she has been used exclusively for sail training and promotional purposes.

BNS Zénobe Gramme, a 29 m (92 ft) Bermuda Ketch, is owned and operated by the Belgian Navy. The ship has been adopted by the Bruxelles Royal Yacht Club. Her home port is the Belgian Naval base in Zeebrugge. The crew consists of one Officer, six crewmembers and ten trainees. She participated in The Tall Ships Races for the first time in 1972 and has been a regular participant ever since. She won the Cutty Sark Trophy in 1976 and the Hans Reith Memorial Trophy and the Sail Training International Ince Trophy in 2003. She has covered 300.000 nautical miles (557.000 km) since 1961. www.mil.be\navycomp

ZVEZDA - The Tall Ships Races

CLASS: C
FLAG: RUSSIA
LENGTH: 16.8M
RIG: BM KETCH
YEAR BUILT: 1935
HOME PORT: ST PETERSBURG
ENTERED BY: ST PETERSBURG RIVER YACHT CLUB
LOCATION: MARINA

*

Zvezda was built in Germany in 1935. Originally she was given the name Stella Polaris and rigged as a Bermudian sloop. It was rumored that at that time she belonged to the LuftWaffe. After World War II Stella Polaris was transferred to Russia as part of an indemnity. She was renamed Zvezda and since then has belonged to St. Petersburg River Yacht Club, governed by Trade Union. For several years she was used as a training ship by the Child Yachting School. Now Zvezda is maintained and operated completely on a voluntary basis. The vessel took part in The Tall Ships Races in 1996 and 2009. ig-dement@yandex.ru

DASHER - The Tall Ships Races

CLASS: D
FLAG: UK
LENGTH: 16.46M
RIG: BM CUTTER
YEAR BUILT: 1977
HOME PORT: GOSPORT, UK
ENTERED BY: JSASTC
LOCATION: MARINA

Dasher is a Nicholson 55 owned by the Joint Services Adventurous Sail Training Centre.

JSASTC presently operates twenty four Sail Training vessels of which three are ocean-going Challenge 67s, six are Nicholson 55s and fifteen are Victoria 34s. Expeditions are arranged for all service levels and are based either at JSASTC, elsewhere in the UK or overseas. Current expeditions have recently included deployments to the Channel area, Scotland, Croatia, Bosnia, Naples, the Caribbean, South America and the USA.

JSASTC also own Chaser and Adventure which, like Dasher, have entered many previous Tall Ships Races.
www.jsastc.org

*

ELENA - North Sea Tall Ships Regatta

Elena is a Bermudan ketch. Built in 1991, her home port is St Petersburg, Russia.

CLASS: D
FLAG: RUSSIA
LENGTH: 13.54M
RIG: BM KETCH
YEAR BUILT: 1991
HOME PORT: ST PETERSBURG
ENTERED BY: INTERNATIONAL BALTIC SAILING CENTRE
LOCATION: MARINA

LIVING NORTH

The *Essence* of Christmas
2010

Don't miss the North of England's most spectacular Christmas Fairs

Living North Christmas Fair
Gosforth Park Racecourse, Newcastle
Thursday 4th November – Saturday 6th November 10.00-17.00
Sunday 7th November 11.00-16.00

Living North Christmas Fair
Hardwick Hall Hotel, Sedgefield, County Durham
Friday 12th November – Saturday13th November 10.00-17.00
Sunday 14th November 11.00-16.00

Living North Christmas Fair
Yorkshire Event Centre, Great Yorkshire Showground, Harrogate
Friday 26th November – Saturday 27th November 10.00-17.00
Sunday 28th November 11.00 -16.00

ENDORFINA - The Tall Ships Races & North Sea Tall Ships Regatta

CLASS: D
FLAG: POLAND
LENGTH: 12.4M
RIG: BM SLOOP
YEAR BUILT: 2009
HOME PORT: KAMIEN POMORSKI
ENTERED BY: WOJCIECH KACZOR
LOCATION: MARINA

*

This yacht was built for family cruising on offshore and sheltered waters. She was launched in 2003 and since then neatly tended. Rich navigational equipment guarantees safety sailing and a comfortable indoor pleasant cruise for eight sailors.

www.jamsen.szczecin.pl

HANSA
- The Tall Ships Races & North Sea Tall Ships Regatta

Hansa is a Bermudan sloop, built in 1995. Her home port is La Coruna, Spain.

CLASS: D
FLAG: SPAIN
LENGTH: 18.28M
RIG: BM SLOOP
YEAR BUILT: 1995
HOME PORT: LA CORUNA
ENTERED BY: JOC SERVICIOS NAUTICOS SL
LOCATION: MARINA

*

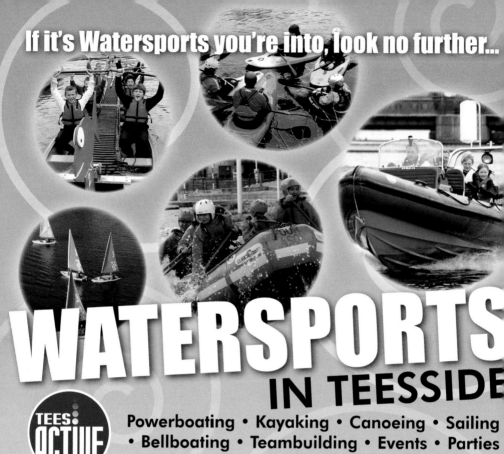

HEBE III - The Tall Ships Races & North Sea Tall Ships Regatta

CLASS: D
FLAG: CZECH REPUBLIC
LENGTH: 11.75M
RIG: BM SLOOP
YEAR BUILT: 1999
ENTERED BY: JJARASLAV HAVELKA
LOCATION: MARINA

Hebe III is a new Jeanneau SunFast 40 Performance, which is based in the Mediterranean. The original Hebe I was built in 1977, Hebe II was built in 1995 and took part in the 1996, 1997 and 1998 Tall Ships Races. Hebe III was built in 1999 and took part in all legs of The Tall Ships Races 2000 and has since been a regular participant in the European races.
www.hebe3.cz

LIETUVA - The Tall Ships Races & North Sea Tall Ships Regatta

Constructed in Gdansk in 1976, this vessel is named after her country (in English her name would be Lithuania). She is owned by the only Lithuanian port city, Klaipeda (the vessel belongs to Klaipeda City Sea Sailing Club).

After the official restitution of Lithuanian Independence, Lietuva was the first vessel to carry the national flag across the oceans.

CLASS: D
FLAG: LITHUANIA
LENGTH: 16.37M
RIG: BM SLOOP
YEAR BUILT: 1976
HOME PORT: KLAIPEDA
ENTERED BY: SPORTO KLUBAS OSTMARINA
LOCATION: MARINA

Lietuva made history in Lithuania by being the first vessel in its history to sail round the world. She also sailed Columbus'92 – among 400 yachts and sailing vessels from all over the world, and came first in the first race and second in the second race of the Transatlantic competition.
www.ostmarina.info

RONA II - The Tall Ships Races & North Sea Tall Ships Regatta

CLASS: D
FLAG: UK
LENGTH: 20.57M
RIG: BM KETCH
YEAR BUILT: 1991
HOME PORT: HAMBLE, ENGLAND
ENTERED BY: RONA SAILING PROJECT
LOCATION: MARINA

The original Rona, a 77' classic ketch, was bought by Lord Amory, then Chancellor of the Exchequer, in the 1960s for the Rona Trust (London Sailing Project), which he had formed to take parties of young sea cadets from London to sea.

The Rona Trust (LSP) now runs the Rona II, Donald Searle and Helen Mary R and takes young people from Scouts, Guides, colleges, sailing clubs, young offender teams,

Social Services and care homes to experience life at sea. The LSP also runs voyages for deaf people, visually impaired people and those with severe learning difficulties.

The aim is to provide, through the medium of sea training in offshore craft, opportunities for young people and people with disabilities, to acquire the key attributes of a seaman – a sense of responsibility, resourcefulness and teamwork – which will help them throughout their lives. www.ronatrust.com

RZESZOWIAK - The Tall Ships Races

CLASS: D
FLAG: POLAND
LENGTH: 13.74M
RIG: BM KETCH
YEAR BUILT: 2000
HOME PORT: GDANSK, POLAND
ENTERED BY: RZESZOWSKI OKREGOWY
LOCATION: MARINA

Rzeszowiak is the property of the Rzeszow Regional Union of Sailors. Rzeszow is a beautiful city in the South of Poland near the Bieszczady Mountains. The name Rzeszowiak (which means a person from Rzeszow) represents the dream of those who live far from the sea but who want to sail. Rzeszowiak was launched in 2000 but construction began in 1988. The hull was built near Rzeszow in Lezajsk over 700km from the sea. The finished hull, with masts, was transported by truck to Gdansk where the vessel was finished and launched.
www.rozz.prz-rzeszow.pl

CLASS: D
FLAG: BELGIUM
LENGTH: 17.54M
RIG: BM SLOOP
YEAR BUILT: 1985
ENTERED BY: TOMIDI CONSULTING N.V
LOCATION: MARINA

TOMIDI
- The Tall Ships Races

This Whitbread Round the World Racer (ex Rucanor) is the only Belgian sail racer ever to have participated twice in this prestigious race (1985/1986 with skipper Staf Verluys and 1989/1990 with skipper Bruno Dubois).

The ship's length overall is 17.54m, the overall beam is 4.85m, and her maximum draft is 2.95m with a displacement of 17 metric tonnes.
www.tomidi.be

URANIA - The Tall Ships Races
& North Sea Tall Ships Regatta

CLASS: D
FLAG: NETHERLANDS
LENGTH: 26.35M
RIG: BM KETCH
YEAR BUILT: 2004
HOME PORT: DEN HELDER, NETHERLANDS
ENTERED BY: MINISTRY OF DEFENCE, THE NETHERLANDS
LOCATION: MARINA

The Royal Netherlands Navy has owned a sail training ship, Urania, since 1830. The name comes from Greek mythology in which Urania was the muse of astronomy. Her crest represents this with the signs of the zodiac and her motto means 'vigilance without fear'.

The current Urania is the sixth and was built in 2003/2004. The lines of Urania are based on the lines of the former Urania to a design of Olivier van Meer, but built to the 2004 standards. She has accommodation for a crew of 17 and is rigged as a ketch. Urania is used as a training ship for training of midshipmen. Urania competed in the Tall Ships Atlantic Challenge 2009 and won the Friendship Trophy for this race series.
www.nlda.nl/kim

Sure Start Children's Centres
Hartlepool

Giving kids the best

start
in life!

Sure Start Children's Centres
are a 'one-stop shop' for
children under five and their
families, where skilled staff
are on hand to give help
and advice.

You can go there for:
- health advice
- parenting and family support
- play sessions and childcare
- help to get a job or training
- a place to meet other parents

Thousands of mums, dads
and children across the country are
already enjoying the benefits.

Families Information
Service **Hartlepool**
http://hartlepool.fsd.org.uk

HARTLEPOOL
BOROUGH COUNCIL

To find your nearest children's
centre call: **01429 284284**

VITYAZ
- The Tall Ships Races & North Sea Tall Ships Regatta

CLASS: D
FLAG: RUSSIA
LENGTH: 11.94M
RIG: BM YAWL
YEAR BUILT: 1971
HOME PORT: ST PETERSBURGH
ENTERED BY: VLADISLAV J POLEZHAEV
LOCATION: MARINA

Vityaz was built at Tallinn's Yacht Yard in 1971, and it is a top-rigged Bermudan sloop. It was built for the one tonne class of yachts for open sea races and long sailing trips. From 1972 Vityaz was the flagship of the Yacht Club of the Baltic Shipping Company based in Leningrad, and the captain was chosen by election each year. Vityaz has sailed each year since then on the Baltic Sea and Lake Ladoga. The current owner was captain of Vityaz from 1985 : sailing on the Baltic Sea from 1985 –1988, and to England and France between 1989 and 1990. In 1996 the Baltic Shipping Company went bankrupt and her former captain bought the ship. Between 1998 and 2002 Vityaz underwent a total reconstruction: the rig was changed to a top tender Yawl rigged and the cabin situation and engine were both changed. From 2003 to 2008 Vityaz sailed again on the Baltic Sea and Lake Ladoga, and the ship first took part in The Tall Ships Races in 2009.

ZRYW - The Tall Ships Races

Within the last 2 years, Zryw sailed twice around the Baltic and once to the northern edge of the Gulf of Bothnia. Then the crew passed the Arctic Circle. Both voyages were rewarded with the local Sailing-tourists Award of the year. Zryw still looks as new, thanks to a hard working and caring crew who have built a strong bond with the yacht.
www.zryw.szczecin.pl

CLASS: D
FLAG: POLAND
LENGTH: 10.57M
RIG: BM SLOOP
YEAR BUILT: 1978
ENTERED BY: CITY OF SZCZECIN
LOCATION: MARINA

EXTENSION OPENING EARLY 2011

EASY IN, EASY OUT

Flexible terms are just one of the benefits on offer at The Innovation Centre Hartlepool

We offer flexible terms and competitive prices in purpose built, thoroughly modern well serviced offices and workshops that leave you free to develop your business without the complex restrictions of a long lease.

- 24 hour access
- 3 Fully equipped meeting & conference rooms
- High speed broadband internet connection
- Network ready Cat 5 intelligent data cabling
- Digital telecom system

- Air conditioning (to the majority of offices)
- Choice of office & workshop units
- Ample free parking
- Sophisticated security system
- Fitness centre
- 'The Mezzanine' - informal relaxation area

For details and availability call Simon Hamilton on:

01429 239500

Or send an email to:
hartlepool@uksteelenterprise.co.uk

The Innovation Centre
Venture Court,
Queens Meadow Business Park,
Hartlepool TS25 5TG

uk steel **enterprise**
INNOVATION CENTRE
H A R T L E P O O L

www.uksteelenterprise.co.uk/hartlepool

North Sea Tall Ships Regatta

As an additional benefit to Hartlepool and spectacle for our visitors, Sail Training International have announced that another race will start from Hartlepool on Wednesday 11th August.

The following information has been provided by Sail Training International:

North Sea Tall Ships Regatta Organised by Sail Training International

Hartlepool, UK: 7th – 10th August 2010 (in-port dates) Race: 11th - 17th August

Estimated time for start of the North Sea Tall Ships Regatta is 1.00pm from Hartlepool on the 11th August.

The final race of the year has been created to form a link between The Tall Ships Races and Sail Amsterdam. The race will start in Hartlepool, UK and finish in IJmuiden, the Netherlands where the ships will gather prior to the Parade of Sail into Amsterdam.

The race will differ from other races run by Sail Training International in that the ships will be offered a number of waypoints around which they can navigate instead of going straight from the start to the finish. The race will be over a set period of time and the ship that has covered the greatest distance in the time allowed, with adjustments made for Time Correction Factors, will be the winner. There will be some 30-40 waypoints from which to choose when planning their route.

Navigators and Captains will need to select waypoints which will suit their own vessels in the forecast weather conditions. This will be a challenging race to sail and also an exciting one to track for those people following the ships' progress.

The idea of the format was first used by STA Netherlands and proved popular with captains and navigators as it provided them with a different set of challenges. Trainees will have their work cut out to help the crews get the best out of their vessel and achieve the aim of covering the greatest distance in the time allowed.

The race will finish on 17th August off the Dutch coast near IJmuiden, where the fleet will then gather with other Sail Amsterdam participants ready for the big Parade of Sail into Amsterdam on 19th August. Only ships which are attending the Sail Amsterdam event will be allowed to take part in the race.

MEMORABILIA STAMPS
be part of it!

Remember what a great day you had at The Tall Ships Races and complete your official visitors' event guide with stamps from your favourite ships.

**TALL SHIPS
STAMPS**

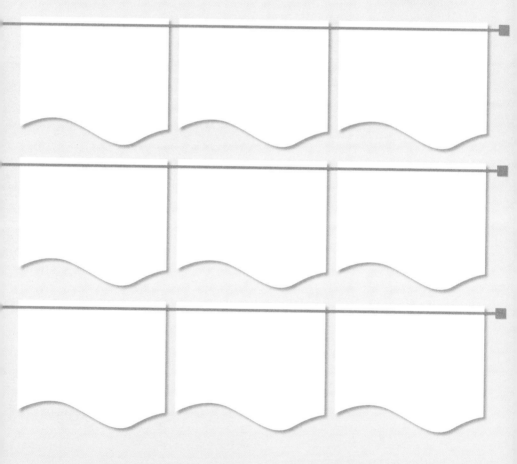

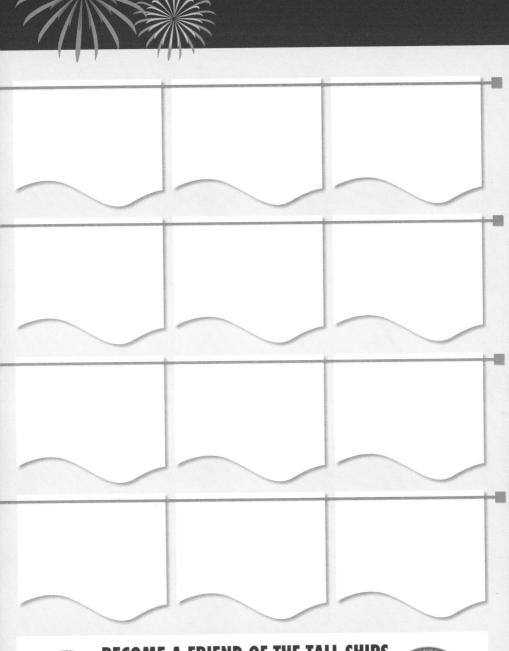

BECOME A FRIEND OF THE TALL SHIPS
www.fots.org

Are you looking for Luxury Office Space in the North East?

We can provide an internal fitting out service to suit your every requirement

---

Fully customised office space available stud walling, partitioning, decorating etc

---

Flexible lease terms | Fantastic incentives

Newcastle | Stockton | Durham

View our full portfolio at
www.mandale.com

CONTACT

t   01642 605514
m 07875 224982
a   Mandale House, 11 Cheltenham Road
    Portrack Interchange Business Park
    Stockton on Tees TS18 2AD
e   simonrobinson@mandale.com

MANDALE
GROUP
www.mandale.com

Official Tall Ships
Merchandise

The Tall Ships Races 2010 – Official Merchandise

ONSITE

Interested in The Tall Ships Races merchandising? There is a fantastic range of well designed, keenly priced merchandising throughout this amazing Tall Ships arena.

We have custom built mobile merchandising stores positioned in the best possible locations, to ensure that wherever you are, the gifts and souvenirs that grab your attention, will be close-by and readily available.

SEND US AN EMAIL

Tell us who you bought for:
mygift@thetallshipsstore.com

WHERE TO FIND US

The six positions within the Tall Ships arena are as follows:

❶ **Fire Zone** – The Tall Ships Village

❷ **Earth Zone** – The Tall Ships Village

❸ **Wind Zone** – The Tall Ships Village

❹ **Navigation Point** – Hartlepool Marina

❺ **Maritime Experience** – Car Park

❻ **The Headland**

Please note, these sites will all be located next to the Information Points

HOW WILL I KNOW WHAT THE OFFICIAL MERCHANDISE STORE LOOKS LIKE?

The Merchandising Service is provided by Official Merchandising Limited
"Make Sure It's Official" www.officialmerchandising.com

Official Tall Ships
Merchandise

The Tall Ships Races 2010 – Official Merchandise
ONLINE

To compliment the comprehensive range of merchandising available throughout the Tall Ships arena, we have built a state of the art, user friendly web store to make available the full range of clothing, gifts and souvenirs.

If after visiting the site, you have forgotten 'wee Johnny's t-shirt' worry not! If the tea-towel Granny wanted was sold out, fear not, just visit:

www.thetallshipsstore.com

What could be simpler!   The online store will be open 24 hours a day, seven days a week. We never close!

There will also be a range of clothing and products that have been exclusively designed for 'the web', therefore, even if Granny got her tea-towel and Johnny's happy!, it's still worth visiting the online store for all the latest offers and limited edition items.

SEND US AN EMAIL

Tell us who you bought for:
mygift@thetallshipsstore.com

The web store was built and supplied by Official Merchandising Limited
"Make Sure It's Official"   www.officialmerchandising.com

LIVING NORTH
ALWAYS FLOATS YOUR BOAT!

SUBSCRIBE TODAY

CALL OUR HOTLINE ON
01434 609933
OR ORDER ONLINE AT
WWW.LIVINGNORTH.COM

BEST VALUE FOR MONEY

Name Mr / Mrs / Miss _____

Address _____

_____

_____

Postcode _____

Telephone _____

email _____

Signature _____

Magazine issue to start subscription
September (published August 11th) ☐
October (published September 8th) ☐

Subscribe for a friend
Please send my subscribed copies to:

Name Mr / Mrs / Miss _____

Address _____

_____

_____

Postcode _____

How to pay
by cheque, postal order or credit card:

United Kingdom ☐ 12 issues = £29.50 with **FREE** p&p

Please telephone, fax or email us for details
for overseas subscriptions.

Living North, 5 Cattle Market, Hexham,
Northumberland NE46 1NJ
Tel: 01434 609933, fax: 01434 600066
email: livingnorth@btconnect.com
www.livingnorth.com

I enclose my cheque/postal order, made payable
to Living North, or debit:

☐ Mastercard ☐ Visa ☐ Maestro

Card No.
☐☐☐☐ ☐☐☐☐ ☐☐☐☐ ☐☐☐☐ ☐☐☐☐

Expiry Date ☐☐ ☐☐

Start Date ☐☐ ☐☐   Issue number

Card Security Code ☐☐☐ (last three digits)

Top Tips

Travel Tips

1. We are expecting the Park & Ride and Park & Walk sites to be very busy in the evening when the days events are finished so please allow for possible delays in your return journey.

2. Remember when travelling back on the Park & Ride to catch your bus from the same place that you were dropped off as there are two drop off points and they deliver to different car parks.

3. For regular traffic updates throughout the Tall Ships event listen to BBC Tees on 95FM, Radio Hartlepool on 102.4FM and Real Radio on 100-102FM.

4. Make sure you have Bluetooth switched on as the BBC will be providing regular information updates via your mobile phone.

5. The Lock Gates in the Marina will be closed throughout the event to pedestrians.

6. If you are travelling by rail, please check the special Tall Ships timetables to make sure you don't miss your last train!

Entertainment Tips

1. Enjoy three nights of spectacular fireworks, 9.45pm on 7th, 8th & 9th August.

2. Consult the event map at the back of this guide for the locations of the performance areas.

3. All events and exhibitions are free unless otherwise stated.

4. Look on the map in this guide for locations of attractions or ask at an Information Point for details.

General Tips

1. Travel light and leave big bags at home – people may be searched by stewards on entry.

2. Alcohol is only permitted in the designated bar areas. No alcohol is permitted to be brought onto or taken off The Tall Ships Village.

3. There are cash points within The Tall Ships Village site.

4. Cash points are also located near to The Tall Ships Village at Navigation Point and ASDA.

5. Dogs are only allowed on the site on a lead. Do not leave dogs in the car.

6. Look out for the information points and information boards around the main site

7. Give children contact details for yourself or other guardians if they get lost. Lost Persons are located next to Information Points around the site. Children's wristbands will be distributed at the Information Points.

8. Watch out for staff on hand to help you at the event, yellow T-shirts for Event Staff and red for Event Volunteers.

9. If the weather is hot don't forget to bring sun tan lotion and drink plenty of water.

10. As there is a possibility of congestion on the roads, be prepared and make sure you bring along water, food and other essentials.

Access Tips

1. A British Sign Language Interpreter will be available at the Information Point in the Fire Zone in The Tall Ships Village.

2. Shopmobility is located in the Fire Zone in The Tall Ships Village.

3. The Class A ship Tenacious has been specifically adapted to provide access throughout for people with disabilities including wheelchair users, with flat wide decks and powered lifts. There is also a speaking compass and bright track radar, induction loop and vibrator alarms.

4. Accessible toilets are available in each toilet location around the site.

5. Adult changing facilities are available at the Havelock Day Centre, Warren Road Day Centre and Central Library.

Competition

You've seen it, you've enjoyed it, you want to come back!

Why not enter our competition to win £100 towards a meal at the restaurant of your choice in Hartlepool and make a repeat visit to our town.

Hartlepool offers an extensive choice of delicious cuisine to satisfy any taste. Be it the Marina, Town Centre, Seaton Carew or a village setting, you will find superb restaurants, cafes, bars and pubs offering food from around the world.

To enter our competition simply log onto our website www.destinationhartlepool.com/tallships and sign up for your chance to win. The closing date for entries is 30th September 2010.

The winner will be notified after this date and given the opportunity to choose the restaurant where they would like to spend the £100 prize.

2 for 1 Offer in Hartlepool's Maritime Experience

If you did not manage to make it to Hartlepool's Maritime Experience then you don't know what you are missing. And if you did ....you know you must come back and visit again.

This award-winning attraction allows you to step back in time to life in an 18th century seaport and also visit Hartlepool's very own tall ship, HMS Trincomalee, the oldest warship afloat in the Europe.

Terms and conditions:- Bring your event guide to reception to receive 2 tickets for the price of 1, cheapest ticket free of charge, valid from August 11th 2010 until March 31st 2011. Not to be used in conjunction with any other offer or on Bank Holidays.

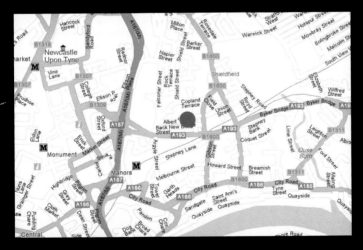

Event Map

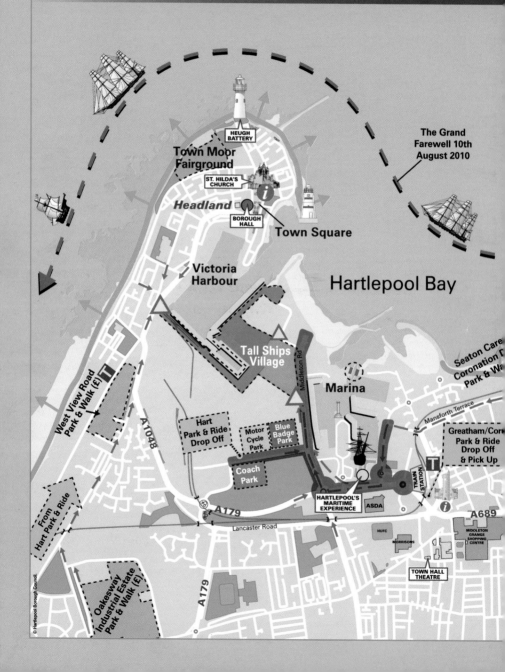

The Grand
Farewell 10th
August 2010

HEUGH
BATTERY

Town Moor
Fairground

ST. HILDA'S
CHURCH

Headland

BOROUGH
HALL

Town Square

Victoria
Harbour

Hartlepool Bay

Tall Ships
Village

Middleton Rd

Marina

Seaton Care
Coronation D
Park & Wa

West View Road
Park & Walk (E)

A1048

Hart
Park & Ride
Drop Off

Motor
Cycle
Park

Blue
Badge
Park

Mansforth Terrace

Greatham/Cor
Park & Ride
Drop Off
& Pick Up

From
Hart Park & Ride

Coach
Park

HARTLEPOOL'S
MARITIME
EXPERIENCE

ASDA

TRAIN
STATION

A179

A179

Lancaster Road

HUFC

MORRISONS

A689

MIDDLETON
GRANGE
SHOPPING
CENTRE

TOWN HALL
THEATRE

Oakesway
Industrial Estate
Park & Walk (E)

© Hartlepool Borough Council